MATHS NOW! 6

GET THE POINT!

GREEN ORBIT

MATHS NOW! 6

GET THE POINT!

GREEN ORBIT

TONY &
MARY ELLEN BELL

JOHN MURRAY

Titles in this series:

Maths Now! Get the Point! Pupil's 1	0 7195 7276 2
Maths Now! Get the Point! Teacher's Resource File 1	0 7195 7277 0
Maths Now! Get the Point! Pupil's 2	0 7195 7278 9
Maths Now! Get the Point! Teacher's Resource File 2	0 7195 7279 7
Maths Now! Get the Point! Pupil's 3	0 7195 7352 1
Maths Now! Get the Point! Teacher's Resource File 3	0 7195 7353 X
Maths Now! Get the Point! Pupil's 4	0 7195 7354 8
Maths Now! Get the Point! Teacher's Resource File 4	0 7195 7355 6
Maths Now! Get the Point! Pupil's 5	0 7195 7356 4
Maths Now! Get the Point! Teacher's Resource File 5	0 7195 7357 2
Maths Now! Get the Point! Pupil's 6	0 7195 7358 0
Maths Now! Get the Point! Teacher's Resource File 6	0 7195 7440 4

First published in 2001
by John Murray (Publishers) Ltd
50 Albemarle Street
London W1S 4BD

Layouts by Stephen Rowling/springworks.
Artwork by Tom Cross, Mike Flanagan, Mike Humphries, Janek Matysiak.
Cover design by John Townson/Creation.

Typeset in 12/14pt Times by Wearset, Boldon, Tyne and Wear.
Printed and bound by G. Canale, Torino, Italy.

A CIP catalogue record for this book is available from the British Library.

ISBN 0 7195 7358 0
Teacher's Resource File 6 0 7195 7440 4

Contents

Acknowledgements

Cover Corbis/Stockmarket; **p.8** *tl* ©Alan Schein/Corbis/Stockmarket, *tr* ©Peter Harholdt/Corbis, *ml* ©Corbis/Stockmarket, *m* ©Kevin R. Morris/Corbis, *mr* ©Bill Sumner/Corbis/Stockmarket, *bl* ©Lynn Goldsmith/Corbis, *bm* Peter Trievnor/Rex Features Limited, *br* Last Resort Picture Library; **p.11** *l-r* ©D.R. Stoecklein/Corbis/Stockmarket, Chat Magazine/Rex Features Limited, ©Michael Keller/Corbis/Stockmarket, ©Corbis/Stockmarket; **p.13, 22, 23, 24, 28** *all* Last Resort Picture Library; **p.31** Celador Productions Limited; **p.34** © John Townson/Creation; **p.37** *t* Claude Nuridsany and Marie Perennou/Science Photo Library, *all others* ©John Townson/Creation; **p.42** Reproduced by permission of Geographers' A–Z Map Co. Ltd. Licence No. B0980. This product includes mapping data licensed from Ordnance Survey ®. ©Crown Copyright 2001. Licence number 100017302; **pp.50, 52** *all* Last Resort Picture Library; **p.58** David Hodges/Rex Features Limited; **p.59** *tl* Doug Pensinger/Allsport, *tm* Heinz-Harald Frentzen/Allsport, *tr* Stuart Clarke/Rex Features Limited, *bl and br* ©Sally Greenhill; **p.64** *bm* Patrick Eagar Photography, *all others* ©John Townson/Creation; **pp.70, 71** *all* ©John Townson/Creation; **p.80** Last Resort Picture Library; **p.85** Rex Features Limited; **pp.93, 109** *all* Last Resort Picture Library; **p.110** ©John Townson/Creation; **pp.111, 114, 117, 121, 122,** *all* Last Resort Picture Library; **p.129** © BBC

l = left, r = right, t = top, m = middle, b = bottom

The authors would like to thank Kim O'Driscoll, Researcher in low attainment in mathematics, University of Strathclyde, and all the schools and teachers throughout the country who helped in the development of this book.

How to use this book

This maths book is planned to help you understand and enjoy maths. You will be able to gain points which you will collect on a sheet so that you can see how well you are doing. You can swap these points for rewards.

In this book you will meet some symbols. They will tell you what you need and what to do. Here they are.

Work with a partner

Work in a group

See your teacher

Fetch equipment

Take a test

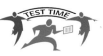

Stop and think

Copy and complete

When you **copy and complete**, replace a box □ with a number and a line ____________________ with a word or words.

Sometimes you are given an example to show you how to start. These are always written in red, like this.

We hope that you will enjoy this book.

1 Number

Place value to 1 000 000

Unit 1 words

million	**column**	less than
greater than	between	digit
smallest	zero	divide
multiply	total	roughly

Remember

Examples are shown in red.

means copy and complete.

You need

- a set of Unit 1 vocabulary Snap cards.

Play a game of Snap to help you learn the words.

Try the **word test** to get some points.

1 Use **all** the digits **0 8 3 1** to make a number:

a) greater than 8000
b) less than 2000
c) between 3000 and 4000
d) between 1500 and 2000

2 How many **digits** are there in these numbers?

a) 3 = □ digit
b) 310 = □ digits
c) 3001 = □ digits
d) 31 = □ digits
e) 30 001 = □ digits
f) 300 010 = □ digits
g) The **smallest** number is □.
h) The **largest** number is □.
i) Put the numbers in order – **smallest** number first.
j) Would the numbers above still have the same value **without the zeros**?

3 From Question 2a) to f) above, take out the zeros and write the new numbers in **digits** and **words**.

4 Choose the correct **number** to match the **words**.

One hundred and sixty thousand and fifty-four.

a) 160 000 54 or 160 54 or 160 054

One thousand two hundred and five.

b) 1200 5 or 1205 or 1 000 205

Four hundred and sixty thousand.

c) 400 60 or 460 000 or 400 60 000

Sixty thousand and fourteen.

d) 60 00014 or 6 000 014 or 60 014

Eighty thousand and two.

e) 8 002 or 80 002 or 80 000 2

Remember

When we find a number **roughly**, we say we **round** it.

5 Round to the **first** digit and write in words:

a) 352 853 rounds to 400 000 – four hundred thousand

b) 65 c) 310 d) 686

e) 5312 f) 2009 g) 13 000

h) 58 742 i) 239 814 j) 52

6 a) 9 + 1 b) 90 + 1 c) 90 + 10

d) 900 + 10 e) 900 + 100 f) 9000 + 10

g) 9000 + 100 h) 9000 + 1000 i) 90 000 + 1000

j) 90 000 + 10 000

You need

- a calculator.

k) 900 000 + 100 000

l) What do you think the **next two** numbers **after** 999 999 will be? Check on your calculator.

> **Remember**
>
> 1 000 000 is called a million.

7 What is the number:

a) one less than a million?

b) a hundred more than 900 000?

c) ten less than 1000?

d) one more than 99 000?

8 You need

- a calculator.

See what happens when you enter:

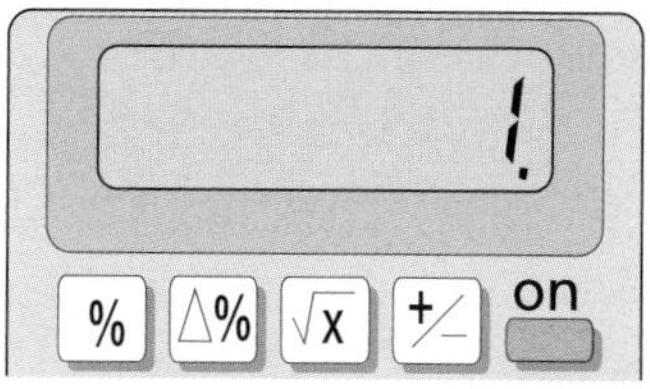

a) [×] [10] and press [=]

b) [×] [10] again, and press [=]

c) [×] [10] again, and press [=]

d) [×] [10] again, and press [=]

e) [×] [10] again, and press [=]

f) [×] [10] again, and press [=]

You could write your answers in a table like this:

Million	Hundreds of thousands	Tens of thousands	Thousands	Hundreds	Tens	Units
						1
					1	0
				1	0	0
			1	0	0	0
		1	0	0	0	0
	1	0	0	0	0	0
1	0	0	0	0	0	0

g) What happens to the digit **1** each time?
Why are the zeros important?

h) Enter 1 000 000 (a million) and divide by 10 (6 times). Write down the answers in columns like those above.

> When you say the word **million**, you leave a space and then you must have **six digits**.

9 You need

- a calculator.

Multiply these numbers by 10.
Set your answers out like this:

$20 \xrightarrow{\times 10} 200$

a) 20 b) 2 c) 200 d) 2000

e) 12 f) 102 g) 63 h) 5

i) 117 j) 80 k) 32.1 l) 30

m) 2.5 n) 6.3

o) What do you notice?

p) Try 10 numbers of your own. Guess the answers and see if you are right.

10 You need

- a calculator.

Divide these numbers by 10.
Set your answers out like this:

$20 \xrightarrow{\div 10} 2$

a) 20 b) 2000 c) 200 d) 20 000

e) 120 f) 1020 g) 630 h) 50

i) 117 j) 80 k) 321 l) 30

m) 2.5 n) 6.3

o) What do you notice?

p) Try 10 numbers of your own. Guess the answers and see if you are right.

11 Try Worksheets 1 and 2 *Multiply and divide by tens (1)* and *(2)*.

12 You need

- a calculator.

Multiply these numbers by 100.
Set your answers out like this:

$20 \xrightarrow{\times 100} 2000$

a) 20 b) 2 c) 200 d) 2000

e) 12 f) 102 g) 63 h) 5

i) 117 j) 80 k) 32.1 l) 30

m) 2.5 n) 6.3

o) What do you notice?

p) Try 10 numbers of your own. Guess the answers and see if you are right.

13 You need

- a calculator.

Divide these numbers by 100.
Set your answers out like this:

$200 \xrightarrow{\div 100} 2$

a) 200 b) 20 000 c) 2000 d) 200 000

e) 400 f) 24 000 g) 144 000 h) 1000

i) 900 j) 9800 k) 321 000 l) 30 300

m) 202 000 n) 1100

o) What do you notice?

p) Try 10 numbers of your own. Guess the answers and see if you are right.

14 Try Worksheets 3 and 4 *Multiply and divide by hundreds (1)* and *(2)*.

15 You need

- a calculator.

How many times will you need to press × 10 to change:

a) 10 into 100?

b) 10 into 10 000?

c) 10 into 100 000?

d) 10 into 1 000 000?

e) 100 into 1000?

f) 100 into 100 000?

g) 100 into 1 000 000?

h) 1000 into 100 000?

i) 1000 into 1 000 000?

j) 10 000 into 1 000 000?

Check your answers on your calculator.

16 You need

- a calculator.

Which number do you divide by to change:

a) 1 000 000 to 100 000?

b) 100 000 to 10 000?

c) 100 000 to 1000?

d) 1000 to 100?

e) 100 to 10?

f) 10 to 1?

g) 1 to 0.1?

h) 0.1 to 0.01?

17 Write these sums in columns to find the **total**.

a)
$$\begin{array}{r} 300\,000 \\ +70\,000 \\ \hline 370\,000 \end{array}$$

b) 300 000 + 70 000 + 40

c) 300 000 + 70 000 + 40 + 5

d) 100 000 + 5 + 200 + 40 + 70 000

e) 5 + 300 000 + 200 + 1 000 000 + 70 000 + 40

18 Try Worksheet 5 *Put in order*.

19 You need

- a calculator.

Look at the numbers on these two statements.

a) Are they the same?

b) Enter each number into your calculator separately and press = after each one.
What do you notice?

c) Enter each number below into your calculator separately and press = after each one.
000 123 and 123 000
001 020 and 102 000
What do you notice?

20 Try Worksheet 6 *Tens and hundreds around.*

21 If you won a million pounds, what could you do with the money?

How many different ways could you spend it?
You can find out some costs of your own or choose from the following.
Round to the first digit to work out roughly or use a calculator.

Cruise – £3280

£65 600

£980 000

£190 000

£135 000

£640 000

£320 000

Dine out with a friend every evening for a year – £30 000

Now try Unit 1 Test.

Review 1

1 Put these numbers in order and find the **median** or **middle** values:

a) 15 cm 30 cm 44 cm 102 cm 65 cm 80 cm 20 cm

b) 1 kg 9 kg 17 kg 6 kg 7 kg 5 kg 14 kg

c) If the sizes of these shoes were covered up, what is the **probability** or **chance** of taking out a pair of **size 5**?

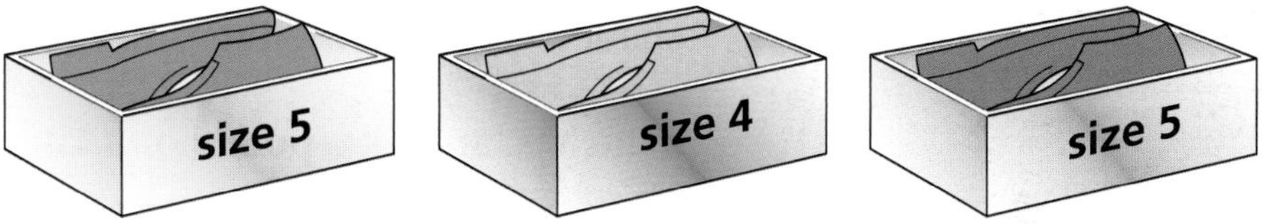

☐ out of ☐ or ☐/☐

2 A night out for **one** person costs £29. How much would it cost for a group of:

a) three? b) nine? c) six?

d) seven? e) ten?

3 a) **cm³** is a short way of writing __________ __________.

b) How many **cm³** does this shape take?

☐ cm³

4 a) Write the shaded part as a **fraction**, a **decimal** and a **percentage** (%).

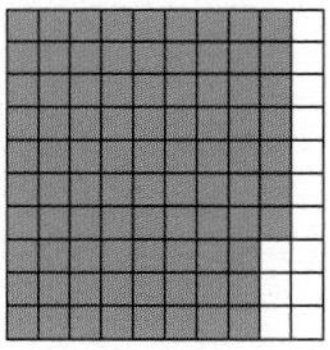

b) If three more hundredths $\frac{3}{100}$ were shaded, write the new shaded part as a **fraction**, a **decimal** and a **percentage** (%).

5 a) Which is larger – a **pound** or a **kilogram**?

Write down something which measures:

b) 1 cm   c) 1 m   d) 1 kg   e) 1 litre

Remember these to help you guess measures.

2 Handling data

Reading more graphs

Unit 2 words

key	**highest**	**lowest**
least	smallest	temperature
different	median	range
pictogram	maximum	month

Remember

Examples are shown in red.

means copy and complete.

You need

- a set of Unit 2 vocabulary Snap cards.

Play a game of Snap to help you learn the words.

Try the **word test** to get some points.

1 a) Because we have a range of different temperatures in Britain, people wear different clothes at different times of the year.

A

B

C

D

Which clothes in the pictures above match the temperatures below?

W −2 °C **X** 22 °C **Y** 14 °C **Z** 30 °C

b) Write, in °C, roughly how cold and how hot you think it could get in Britain.

> **Remember**
>
> The **middle** value of data when put in **order** is called the **median** (**i** in middle and **i** in median).

> **Remember**
>
> The difference between the **highest** and **lowest** values is called the **range**.

2 a) Put the temperatures of these places in order to find the **median**.

Aytown
25 °C −5 °C 0 °C −10 °C 35 °C 10 °C 15 °C

Beesville
22 °C 21 °C 25 °C 10 °C 8 °C 15 °C 26 °C

Ceeford
−2 °C 11 °C −5 °C 1 °C 7 °C 9 °C −9 °C

b) What is the **range** of temperature for each place?

c) In which of these places would you most like to live?

3 This pictogram shows the number of people booking with a travel agent in one month to visit these countries.

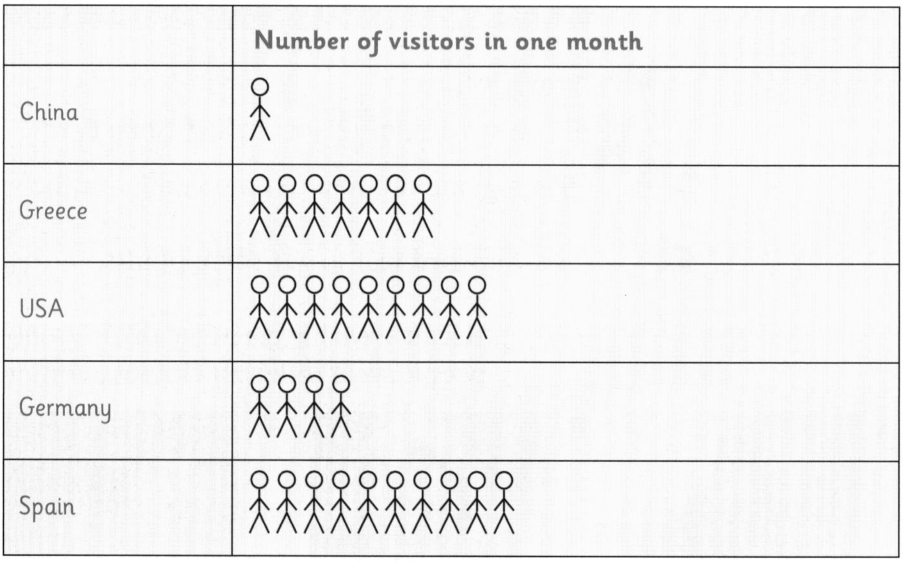

Number of visitors in one month
China
Greece
USA
Germany
Spain

Key:  = 10 people

a) How many people booked to go to each country?

b) Which country was **most** popular?

c) Which country was **least** popular?

How many people would be visiting each country if the key was:

d) = 5 people?

e) = 100 people?

f) = 1000 people?

g) = 10 000 people?

h) = 100 000 people?

i) = 1 000 000 people?

j) Which of the keys do you think may be a sensible one to show the number of people going away to other countries?

4 Now try Worksheets 1 and 2 *Keys (1)* and *(2)*.

5 These six friends are planning to go on holiday together.

Each of them has a favourite place.
The graphs in Questions 6–8 give you information about the six places. For example, they give you the maximum temperature for each month of the year.

Which is the maximum of these temperatures?

A 23 °C **B** 2 °C **C** 15 °C **D** 32 °C

6

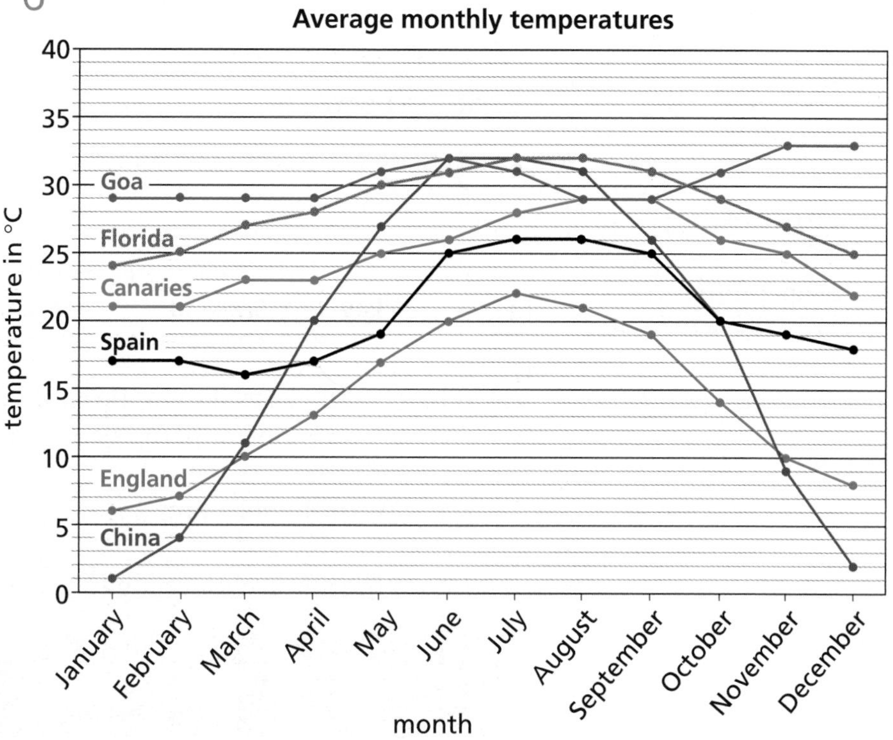

What is the temperature in:

a) Spain in April? b) China in July?

c) The Canaries in December?

What are three of the **warmest** months in:

d) England? e) Florida? f) Spain?

What are three of the **coolest** months in:

g) The Canaries? h) China? i) Goa?

In which places do the temperatures never:

j) drop below 12 °C? k) rise above 26 °C?

Choose **rising** or **falling**. The temperature is:

l) __________ in Goa between March and June.

m) __________ in Florida between September and January.

n) __________ in China between July and September.

o) __________ in England between February and June.

> **Remember**
>
> The difference between the **highest** and **lowest** temperatures is called the **range** of temperature.

p) What is the **range** of temperature in each place?

Which place has the:

q) **biggest** range of temperature?

r) **smallest** range of temperature?

7

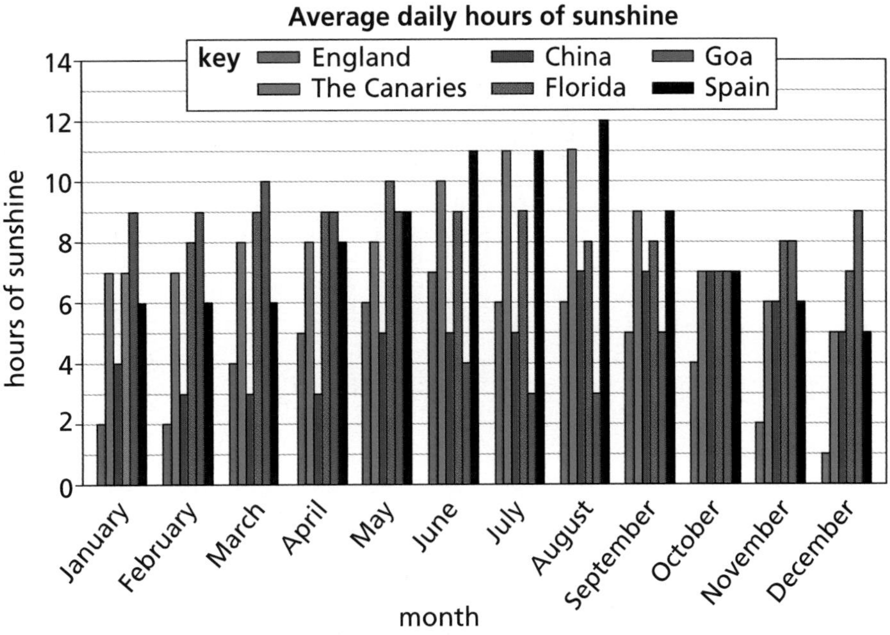

a) Which place, in which month, had **most** hours of sunshine?

b) Which place, in which month, had **least** hours of sunshine?

What are three of the **sunniest** months in:

c) England? d) Florida? e) Spain?

What are three of the **dullest** months in:

f) The Canaries? g) China? h) Goa?

i) In England, in January, there are two hours of sunshine a day. How **many more** hours of sunshine are there in the other places in January?

j) In England, in June, there are seven hours of sunshine a day. How **many more or less** hours of sunshine are there in the other places in June?

k) Which place is the sunniest all year round?

8

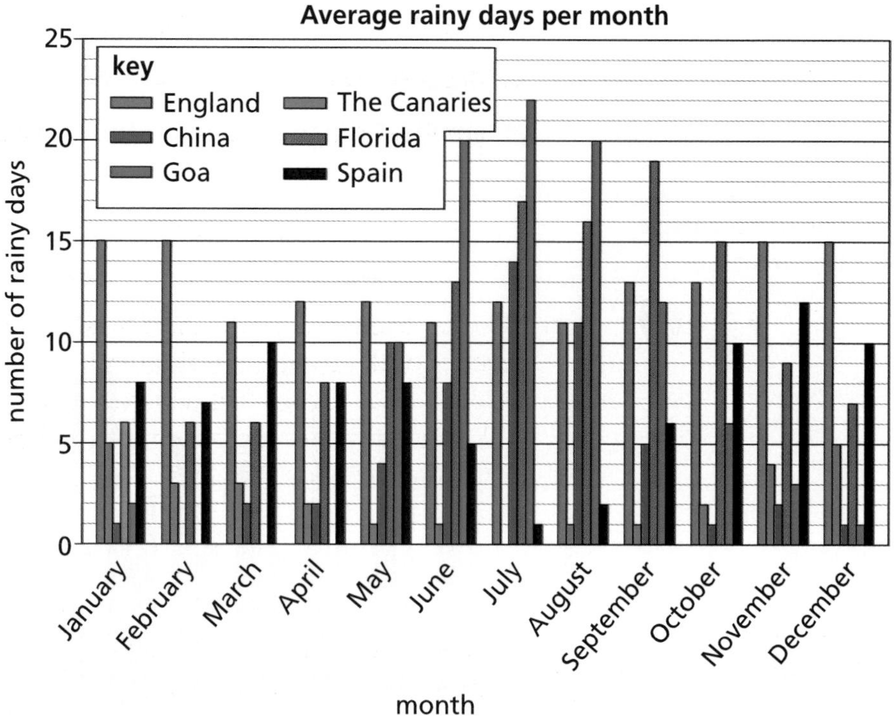

a) Which place, in which month, had **most** rain?

b) Which places, in which months, had **least** rain?

What are three of the **wettest** months in:

c) England? d) Florida? e) Spain?

What are three of the **driest** months in:

f) The Canaries? g) China? h) Goa?

How many **more dry days** are there in July than in January in:

i) England? j) Spain? k) The Canaries?

How many **more wet days** are there in July than in January in:

l) Goa? m) Florida? n) China?

Which place is:

o) **wettest** all year round? p) **driest** all year round?

9 Look at the three graphs in Questions 6–8. Which are the best three months to go on holiday to each of the six places? Decide what sort of holiday you would like to have, e.g., trekking or lying on a beach. Remember to look at all three graphs before you decide.

Remember

When it is wet as well as hot, it is humid – like a greenhouse – and there are a lot of biting insects about.

10 Here are tables of information for more holiday destinations.

Temperature (°C) and cost (£)							
Destination	**Nov**	**Dec**	**Jan**	**Feb**	**Mar**	**Apr**	**Cost**
Spain	19	18	17	17	16	17	£300
The Canaries	25	22	21	21	23	23	£500
Florida	27	25	24	25	27	28	£500
The Gambia	32	31	31	32	34	33	£500
Italy	17	14	13	14	15	17	£750
Goa	33	33	29	29	29	29	£750
Mexico	32	31	31	31	31	31	£750
Austria	1	−1	−2	−3	2	1	£750
The Bahamas	27	26	25	25	26	27	£1000
Jamaica	31	31	30	30	30	31	£1000
South Africa	23	24	26	26	25	22	£1500
Australia	24	25	26	26	25	22	£1500

Number of rainy days and flight time (hours)							
Destination	**Nov**	**Dec**	**Jan**	**Feb**	**Mar**	**Apr**	**Flight time (hours)**
Spain	12	10	8	7	10	8	2
The Canaries	4	5	5	3	3	2	4
Florida	9	7	6	6	6	8	9
The Gambia	1	0	0	0	0	0	6
Italy	7	7	6	5	5	5	4
Goa	3	1	2	0	0	0	11
Mexico	1	1	1	1	1	1	11
Austria	7	9	10	8	9	7	4
The Bahamas	9	6	6	5	5	6	9
Jamaica	5	4	3	3	2	3	10
South Africa	5	3	3	2	3	6	11
Australia	6	6	7	7	8	8	22

Pick a holiday for someone who wants to go somewhere:

a) which is very hot and dry in January – cost £750 – likes long flights

b) which is mild for walking in February – cost £300 – short flight

c) which is hot in March – cost £1500 – flight no longer than 12 hours

d) which is mild for sightseeing in April – cost £300 – short flight

e) which is warm for the beach in February – cost £500 – short flight

f) which is cold for skiing in December – cost £750 – flight four hours

g) hot and dry in November – cost £500 – flight six hours

h) hot and dry in November – cost £1000 – flight of less than 10 hours

i) One person decides on a holiday destination and writes or gives details to a partner. The other person guesses the destination.

11 You need

- Worksheet 3 *Draw a line graph.*

Draw a line graph to show the temperatures from November to April in:

a) Italy　　b) Spain

Draw a line graph to show the rainy days from November to April in:

c) Italy　　d) The Bahamas

12 Try Worksheet 4 *Make a computer database* and Worksheet Puzzle *Take a break.*

Now try Unit 2 Test.

Review 2

1 How many:

a) seconds in 1 minute?
b) seconds in 4 minutes?
c) minutes in 1 hour?
d) minutes in 10 hours?
e) hours in 1 day?
f) hours in 2 days?
g) days in 1 week?
h) days in 8 weeks?
i) complete weeks in 1 month?
j) months in 1 year?

2 What is the **range** of these daily temperatures?

a)
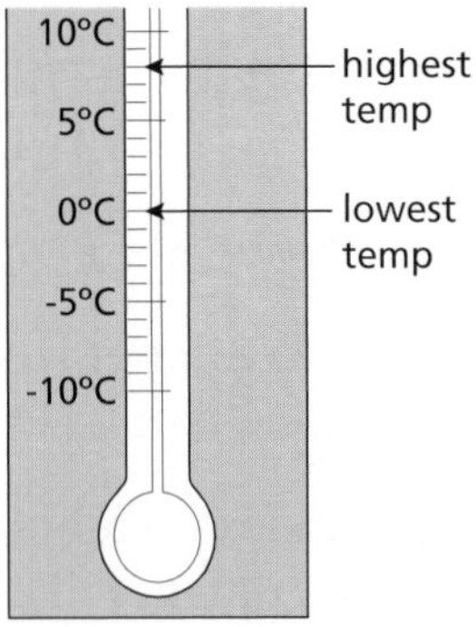

b)
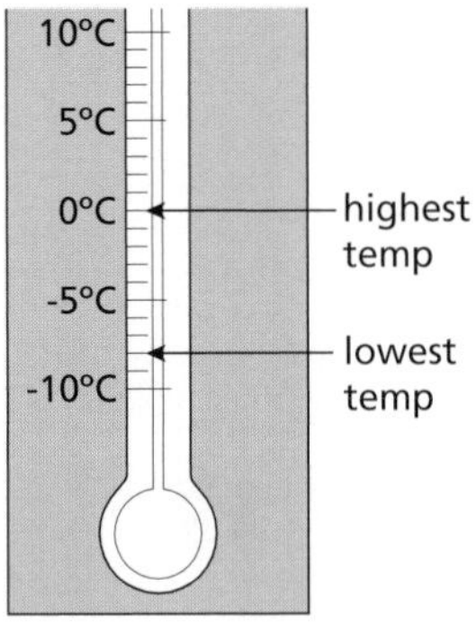

c)
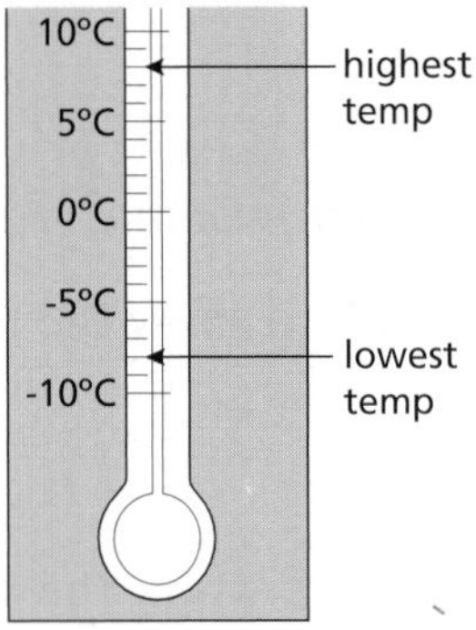

d)
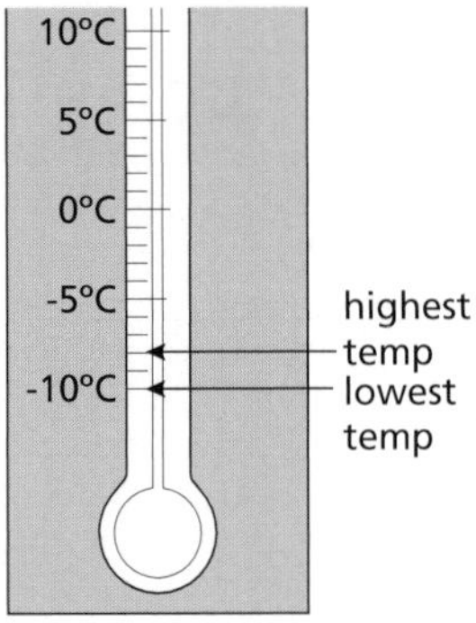

3 You may use a calculator.

How many:

a) minutes in 120 seconds?
b) hours in 300 minutes?
c) days in 168 hours?
d) weeks in 84 days?
e) years in 18 months?

4 Write in **metres** (m):

a) 583 cm b) 500 cm c) 80 cm d) 3 cm

Write in **centimetres** (cm):

e) 0.50 m f) 0.08 m g) 3.00 m h) 3.58 m

i) Measure this line in **centimetres** (cm) and **millimetres** (mm).

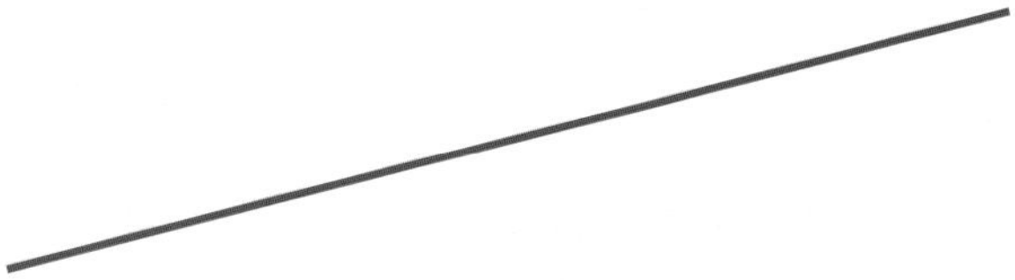

3 Number

Addition and subtraction

Unit 3 words

method	**sum of**	**deposit**
round	balance	subtract
rule	pattern	bigger
smaller	amount	figures

Remember

Examples are shown in red.

✎ means copy and complete.

You need

- a set of Unit 3 vocabulary Snap cards.

Play a game of Snap to help you learn the words.

Try the **word test** to get some points.

1

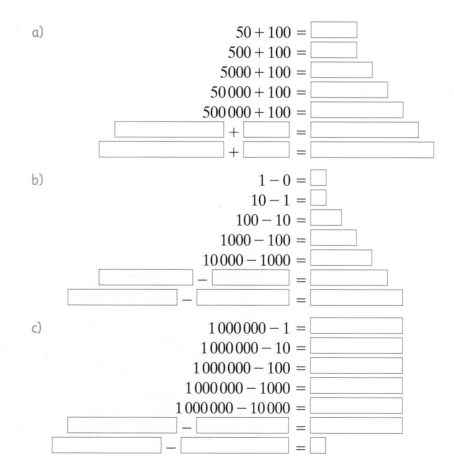

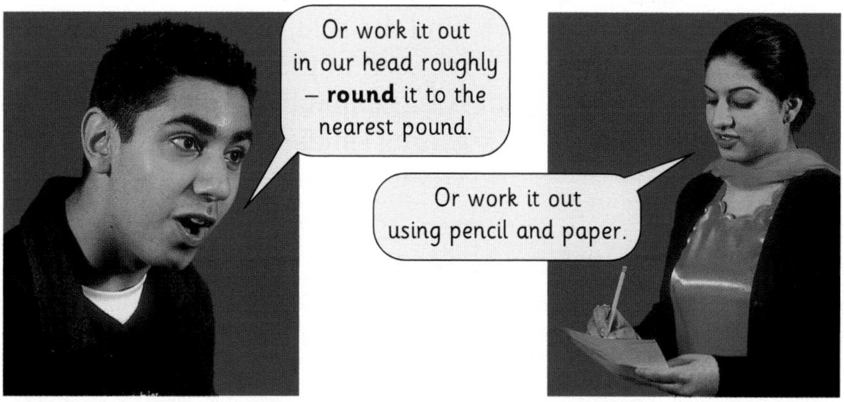

Talk about **when** and **why** you would use all the different methods.

2 Now try Worksheets 1 and 2 *Work it out (1)* and *(2)*.

3 Find the missing answers, and complete the patterns.

a)

$50 + 100 = \square$

$500 + 100 = \square$

$5000 + 100 = \square$

$50\,000 + 100 = \square$

$500\,000 + 100 = \square$

$\square + \square = \square$

$\square + \square = \square$

b)

$1 - 0 = \square$

$10 - 1 = \square$

$100 - 10 = \square$

$1000 - 100 = \square$

$10\,000 - 1000 = \square$

$\square - \square = \square$

$\square - \square = \square$

c)

$1\,000\,000 - 1 = \square$

$1\,000\,000 - 10 = \square$

$1\,000\,000 - 100 = \square$

$1\,000\,000 - 1000 = \square$

$1\,000\,000 - 10\,000 = \square$

$\square - \square = \square$

$\square - \square = \square$

4 Find the rule and continue the pattern (three more numbers) for each of these groups of numbers.
Are the numbers getting **bigger**? Is the rule + or −? Are they getting **smaller**?
Write the rules in words.

a) 300 600 900 [1200] [1500] [1800]

+300 +300 +300 +300 +300

The rule is 'add three hundred'.

b) 501 601 701 801 [ ] [ ] [ ]

c) 9100 9000 8900 8800 [ ] [ ] [ ]

d) 50 500 500 400 500 300 500 200 [ ] [ ] [ ]

e) 190 000 200 000 210 000 220 000 [ ] [ ] [ ]

f) 1 000 000 900 000 800 000 700 000 [ ] [ ] [ ]

Write down **five** numbers which follow the rule:

g) add 1000

h) subtract 100

i) add 10 000

j) subtract 100 000

5 Sal has an account at Hartleys Bank.

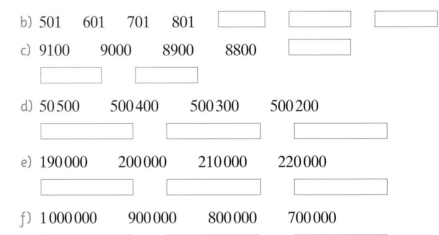

She writes cheques like this.

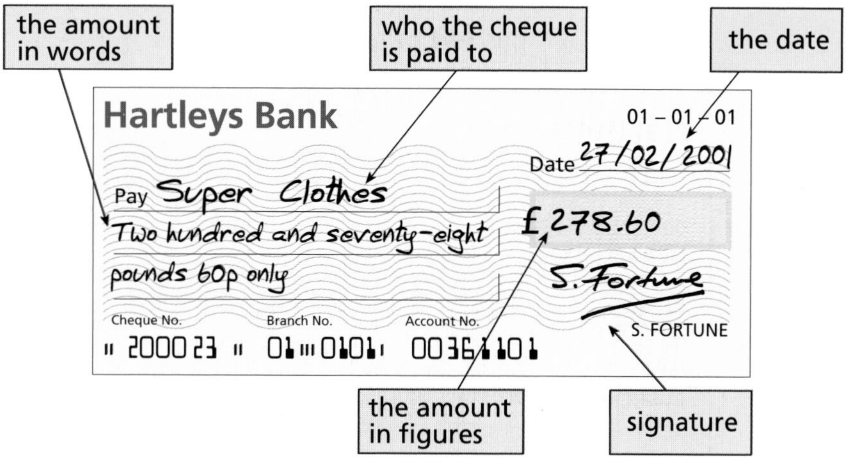

Match each box to the correct letter.

a) Nidd Service Station

b) 20/02/2001

c) S. Fortune

d) 35.00

e) Thirty-five pounds only

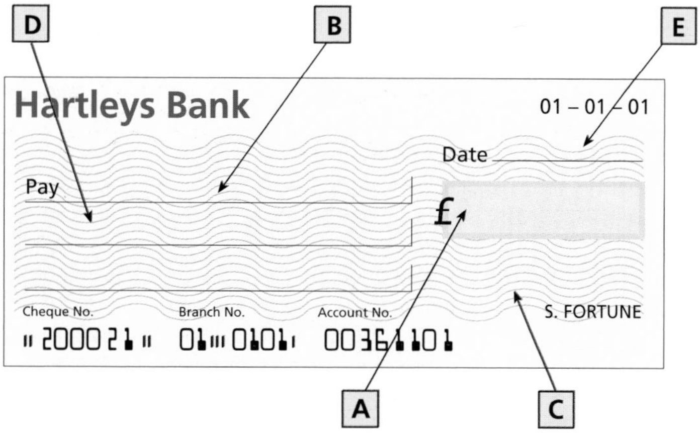

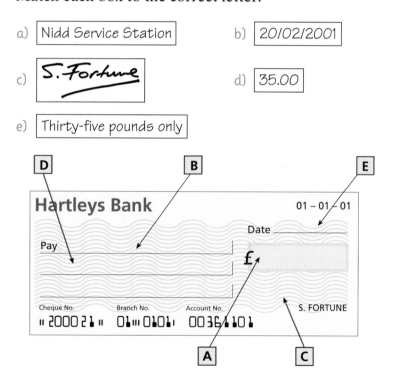

6 Fill in some cheques for Sal – use Worksheet 3 *Bills to pay* and Worksheet 4 *Full cheques*.

7 Sal gets a bank statement.
It tells her how much money she has **spent** and how much she has **left** in her account.

Hartleys Bank

33 East Street
Highgate
London N6 4RJ

000044/054169820
Miss Sal Fortune
2 Craven Court
Highgate
LONDON N6 3MS

Roll No. **F1110111-4**
Sort Code **01-01-01**
Account No. **00361101**

CURRENT ACCOUNT STATEMENT

Date	Description	Payments	Receipts	Balance
	Balance brought forward			£400.73
09/02/01	Standing Order – Internet Services	£5.00		£395.73
12/02/01	Standing Order – Tad Car Insurance	£25.40		£370.33
19/02/01	Switch – Spot Computers	£100.98		£269.35
26/02/01	Cheque – 200021	£35.00		£234.35
	Cheque – 200022	£180.00		£54.35
	Direct Debit – Red Mobile Phones	£25.45		£28.90
27/02/01	Dale's Motors		£875.30	£904.20
04/03/01	Standing Order – Internet Services	£5.00		£899.20
05/03/01	Cheque – 200023	£278.60		£620.60
06/03/01	Switch – Travel USA	£197.00		£423.60
10/03/01	Switch – Nidd Service Station	£39.00		£384.60
12/03/01	Standing Order – Tad Car Insurance	£25.40		£359.20
15/03/01	Cheque – 200025	£129.99		£229.21
24/03/01	Switch – Mid Fashions	£124.13		£105.08
26/03/01	Direct Debit – Red Mobile Phones	£36.40		£68.68
	Cheque – 200026	£31.98		£36.70
27/03/01	Cheque – 200024	£30.00		£6.70
	Dale's Motors		£875.30	£882.00
07/04/01	Cheque – 200029	£45.00		£837.00
09/04/01	Standing Order – Internet Services	£5.00		£832.00
11/04/01	Cheque – 200027	£636.00		£196.00
12/04/01	Standing Order – Tad Car Insurance	£25.40		£170.60
	Balance carried forward			£170.60

where money went (→ Description)

money paid out (→ Payments)

money paid in (→ Receipts)

money left in bank (→ Balance)

In which month:

a) did the statement begin? b) did it end?

c) How much money (balance) was carried forward from the last statement?

Sal gets paid on the **27th** of each month.

d) Where do you think she works?

e) How much pay does she get?

She filled in a form to tell the bank to pay some bills for her each month.

Remember

Payments for the same amount are made by **Standing Orders**.
Payments for different amounts are made by **Direct Debits**.

Who did she pay by:

f) Standing Order? g) Direct Debit?

h) Why do you think she pays by Direct Debit for her mobile phone?

Sal can pay for things using her cheque card.
These show as **Switch** on her statement.

i) List the payments she made using **Switch**.

j) What is the total amount of **Switch payments** she made?

Sal was saving for a holiday in America.
She paid a deposit by **Switch** and a **cheque** for the rest.
How much did she pay for:

k) the deposit? l) the rest?

m) the whole holiday?

n) Could she have saved in a better way for her holiday?

o) What is the balance left to be carried forward?

8 Sal wrote some cheques which have not **cleared** yet.

'Cleared' means that the money has gone from your account.

a) Use Worksheet 3 *Bills to pay* from Question 6 and Worksheet 5 (Help sheet) *Statement* to find out which cheques they are.

When these are cleared:

b) how much money will she have left?

c) what will the balance be?

9 Copy and complete the number line.

Remember

We use the – **sign** to show numbers **less than 0**.
Example: 3 less than 0 is **–3**

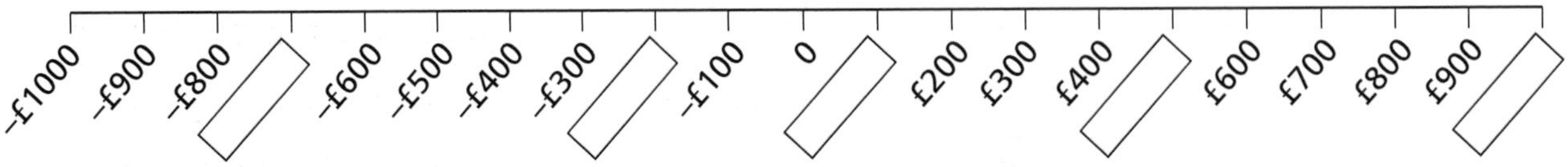

10 Sal sometimes takes money from the cash machine or 'hole in the wall'.

When she takes money she gets this advice slip showing how much money she has left.

Hartleys Bank
ACCOUNT No: 00361101
LOCATION: 01-01-01
HIGHGATE LONDON
WITHDRAWAL: £45.00
ACCOUNT BALANCE:
£00.00
THANK YOU

a) How much did she withdraw?

b) What was the balance **before** she took money out?

This is the advice slip her friend Kev got.

Hartleys Bank
ACCOUNT No: 00873101
LOCATION: 05-04-06
CANAL RD LONDON
WITHDRAWAL: £50.00
ACCOUNT BALANCE:
£-10.00
THANK YOU

c) Why do you think there is a − (minus) sign in the balance?

d) What was the balance before Kev took the money out?

Each of the accounts below had a **balance** of **£1000 before** these withdrawals.
What was the **balance remaining** for each?

e)
Hartleys Bank
ACCOUNT No: E
LOCATION: 22-01-20
WEST RD LONDON
WITHDRAWAL: £650.00
ACCOUNT BALANCE:
£ ______
THANK YOU

f)
Hartleys Bank
ACCOUNT No: F
LOCATION: 38-19-08
RIVER RD LONDON
WITHDRAWAL: £1000.00
ACCOUNT BALANCE:
£ ______
THANK YOU

g)
Hartleys Bank
ACCOUNT No: G
LOCATION: 09-09-09
THAMES ST LONDON
WITHDRAWAL: £1200.00
ACCOUNT BALANCE:
£ ______
THANK YOU

Each of the accounts below had a **balance** of **£500 before** these withdrawals.
How much was **withdrawn**?

h)

Hartleys Bank
ACCOUNT No: H
LOCATION: 05-04-06
CANAL RD LONDON
WITHDRAWAL: £
ACCOUNT BALANCE:
£400.00
THANK YOU

i)

Hartleys Bank
ACCOUNT No: I
LOCATION: 03-03-03
MAIN RD LONDON
WITHDRAWAL: £
ACCOUNT BALANCE:
£50.00
THANK YOU

j)

Hartleys Bank
ACCOUNT No: J
LOCATION: 03-03-03
MAIN RD LONDON
WITHDRAWAL: £
ACCOUNT BALANCE:
£-186.95
THANK YOU

Write the balance for each of these **before** the withdrawals.

k)

Hartleys Bank
ACCOUNT No: K
LOCATION: 50-40-20
SIDE ST LONDON
WITHDRAWAL: £85.50
ACCOUNT BALANCE:
£14.50
THANK YOU

l)

Hartleys Bank
ACCOUNT No: L
LOCATION: 23-23-23
GREEN RD LONDON
WITHDRAWAL: £12 458.00
ACCOUNT BALANCE:
£-58.00
THANK YOU

m)

Hartleys Bank
ACCOUNT No: M
LOCATION: 16-17-18
TUNNEL RD LONDON
WITHDRAWAL: £503.25
ACCOUNT BALANCE:
£96.75
THANK YOU

11 One day you might take part in the television show

'Who wants to be a millionaire?'

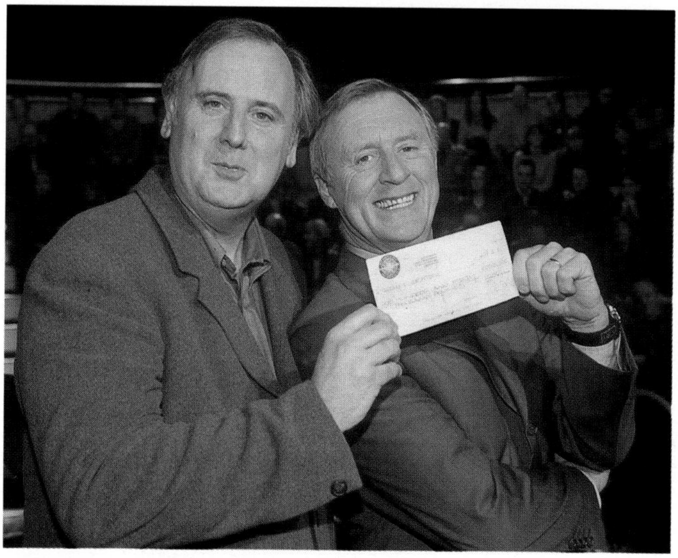

Imagine you have won £1000.

a) Can you double your money until you reach £1 000 000 exactly?

> **Remember**
>
> You can double a number by adding it to itself, or you can multiply it by 2.

b) How near can you get to a million by doubling your money – starting with £1000?

c) How do they get to the £1 000 000 prize on the television show?

12 Now try the **Around addition and subtraction** activity.

Now try Unit 3 Test.

Review 3

1 Find 50% of:

a) 100 cm b) 60 kg c) 4 km d) 1 litre

Find 25% of:

e) £250 f) £160 g) 28 kg h) 4 miles

i) Write the shaded part of each diagram as a **fraction** and a **percentage**.

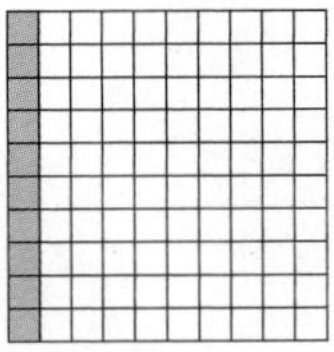

or

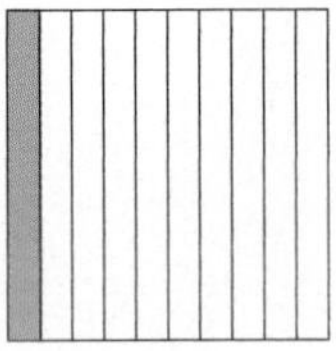

Find 10%, 20%, 40% and 80% of:

j) £20 k) 40 cm l) 300 kg m) 10 hours

2 You need

- an angle measurer.

Measure these angles.

a)

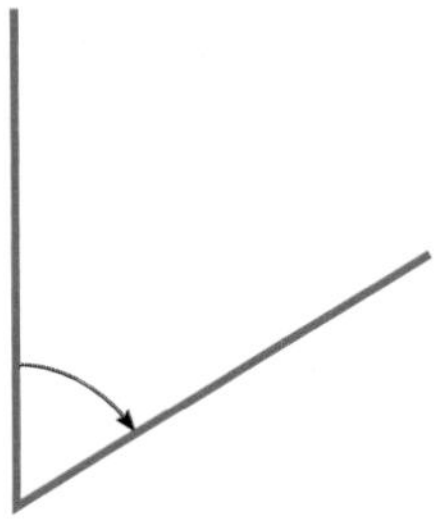

b)

c)

3

6			church			
5						
4	pool		school			shop
3						
2			park			
1						
	A	B	C	D	E	F

a) In which square are each of the marked places?

b) What places are North, South, East and West of the school?

4 If **six** cars – **one** blue, **two** green and **three** red – are in a car park, what is the **chance** or **probability** that:

a) the blue one will leave first?

b) a red one will leave first?

c) a green one will leave first?

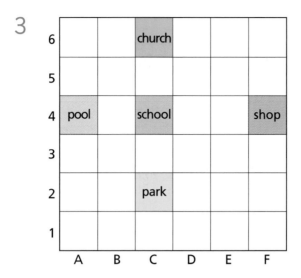

4 Shape and space

Lines and angles

Unit 4 words

full circle	**centre**	**turning symmetry**
compass	right angle	pattern
directions	centimetres	quarter
shapes	exactly	degrees

Remember

Examples are shown in red.

means copy and complete.

You need

- a set of Unit 4 vocabulary Snap cards.

Play a game of Snap to help you learn the words.

Try the **word test** to get some points.

1 Look at the picture of the London Eye wheel on the right. To go round you sit in a 'pod'.

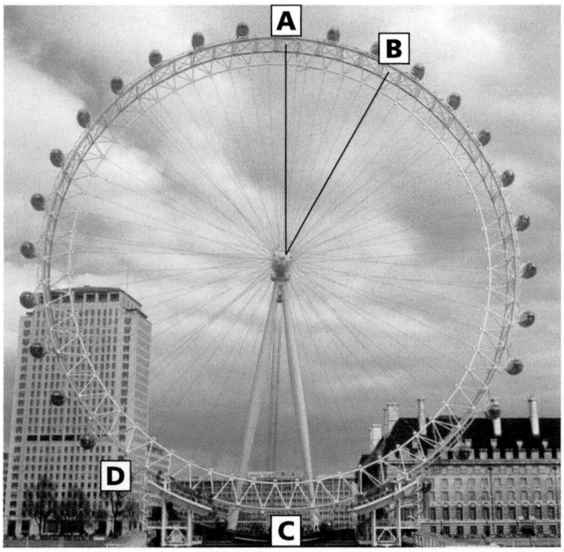

a) If you were sitting in the top pod A and travelled round to pod B, would you have travelled about 30°, 60° or 90°?

b) If you travelled from A to C, would you have travelled about 80°, 180° or 280°?

c) If you travelled from B to C, would you have travelled about 50°, 150° or 250°?

d) If you travelled from A to D, would you have travelled about 80°, 120° or 220°?

e) If you travelled all the way round, you would have travelled a **full circle**. Would this be exactly 180°, 270° or 360°?

2 Fill in the missing numbers: 1, 2, 3 or 4.

a) 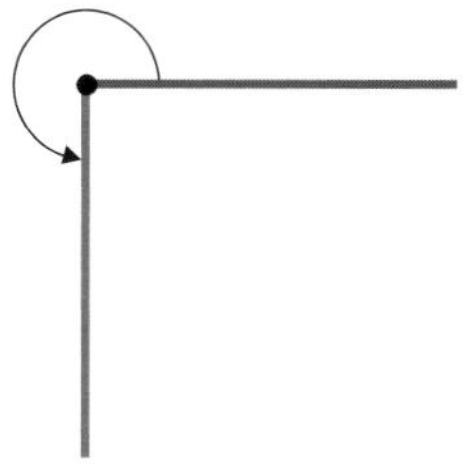 In this turn there are ☐ right angles.

b)  In this turn there are ☐ right angles.

c) 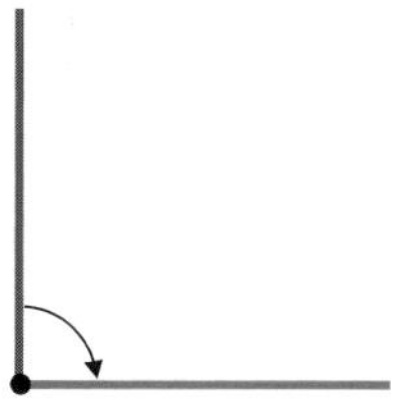 In this turn there is ☐ right angle.

d) 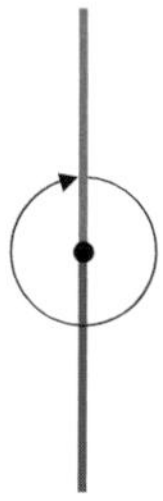 In this turn there are ☐ right angles.

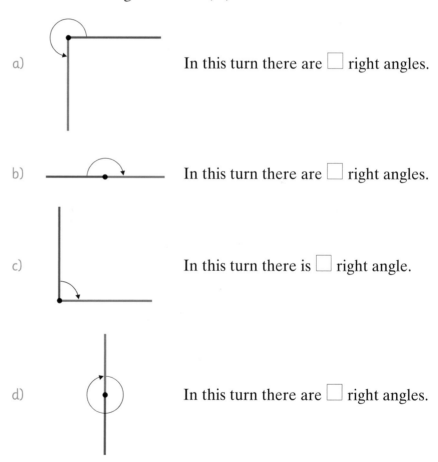

3 Try Worksheet 1 *Measure the angle* and Worksheet 2 *Guess the angle*.

4 Here is a small wheel with only 6 pods.
If you were in pod 1, there would be 6 possible places you could stop.

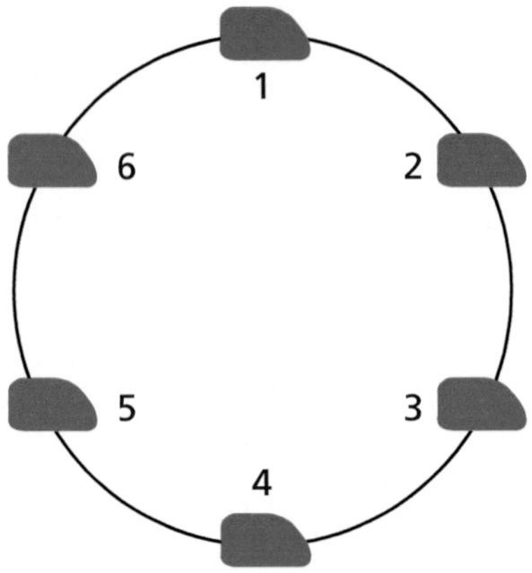

How many places are there to stop for each of these wheels?

a)

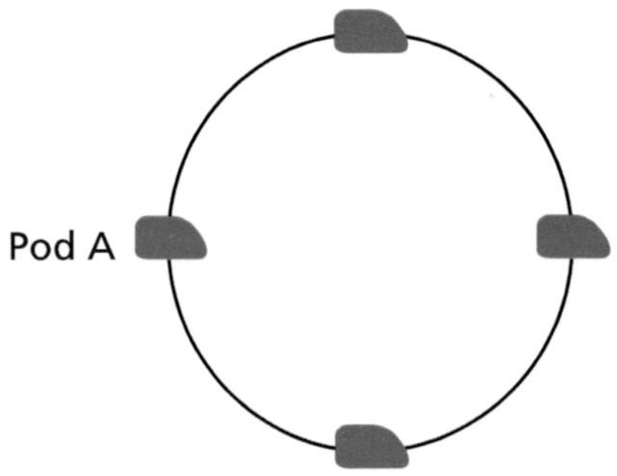

b)

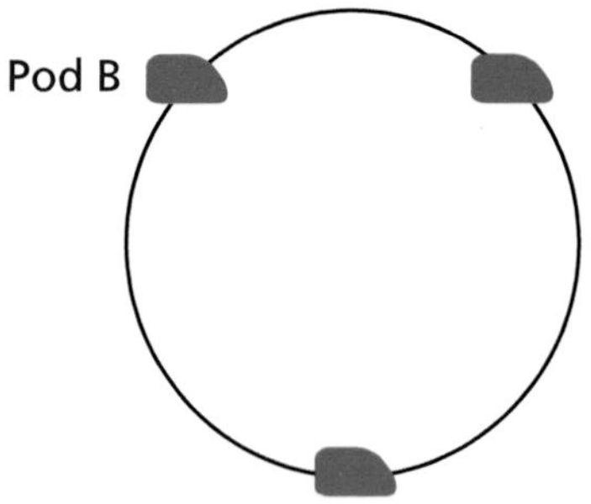

Pod A can stop at ☐ places.   Pod B can stop at ☐ places.

c)

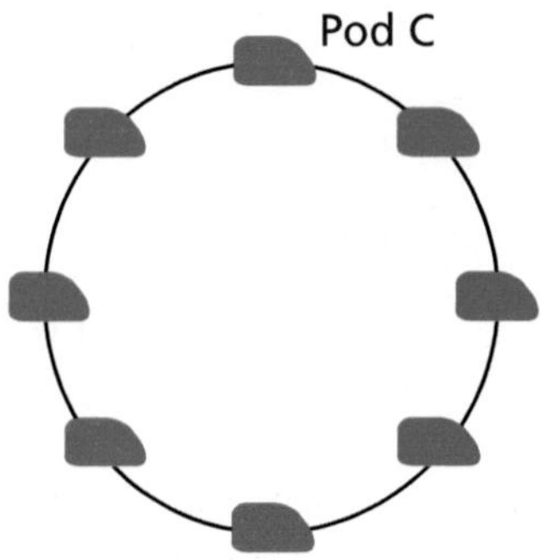

Pod C can stop at ☐ places.

5 Look at these pictures.

They all have a special property.
In each, a shape is repeated around the centre of a circle.

You can make your own turning pattern.

a) Take a piece of centimetre squared paper and draw a square 10 centimetres by 10 centimetres.

b) Divide it into 4 quarters (see below).

c) Draw a pattern in one quarter (see below).

d) Put some tracing paper over the shape and mark the centre.

e) Copy the pattern, turn the paper a $\frac{1}{4}$ of a turn and trace it in the next quarter.

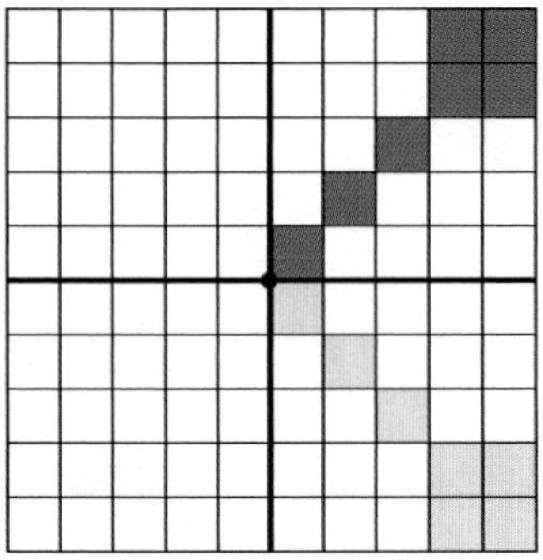

f) Colour in the pattern on the square.

g) Turn the tracing paper another $\frac{1}{4}$ of a turn and trace it in the next quarter.

h) Colour in the pattern on the square.

i) Do this for the last quarter. You should get a pattern like this.

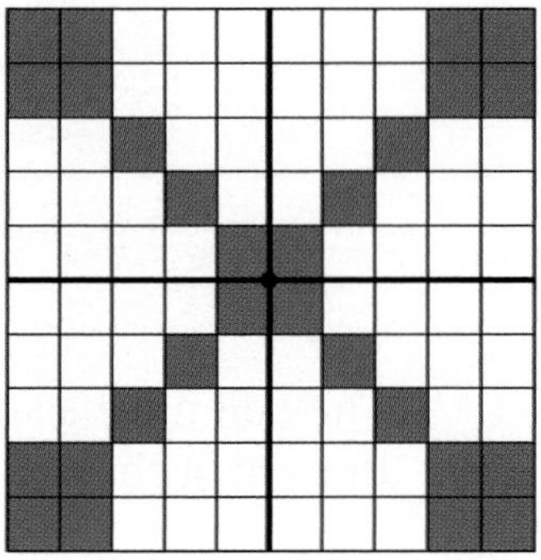

Remember to turn the tracing paper around the centre.

6 Try Worksheet 3 *Turning patterns.*

7 Some shapes have **turning symmetry**.
The **pentagon** has turning symmetry.

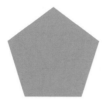

A copy can be placed on top of itself in **five** different ways.

Some shapes can fit on top of themselves in only **one** way.

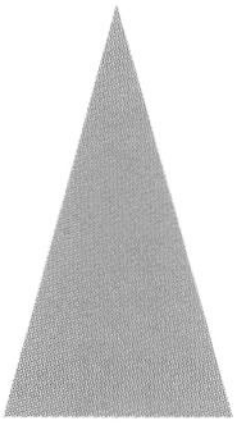

A copy of this triangle can only fit on top of itself **one** way.

How many ways can these shapes fit on themselves?
(You could use tracing paper to help you.)

a)

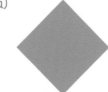

b)

c)

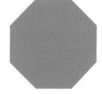

d)

8 Try Worksheet 4 *Turning shapes.*

9 If you were walking somewhere in the wilderness, you could find your way using a compass.

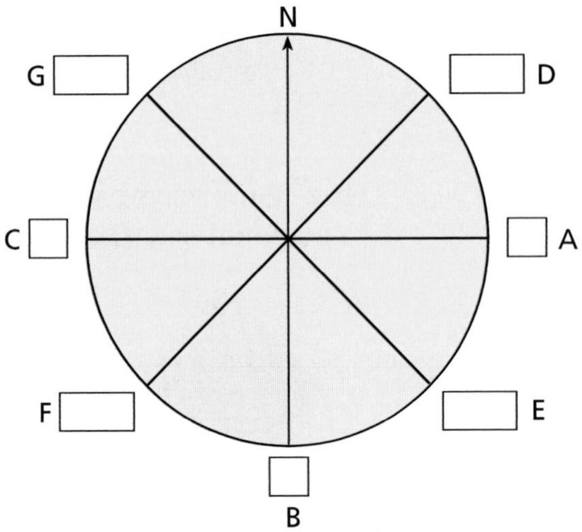

a) Fill in the main compass points at A, B and C.

b) Then fill in the compass points at D, E, F and G.

10 Look at the map below. If you are standing at Buckingham Palace facing North, roughly where are the following (N, S, E or W of you)?

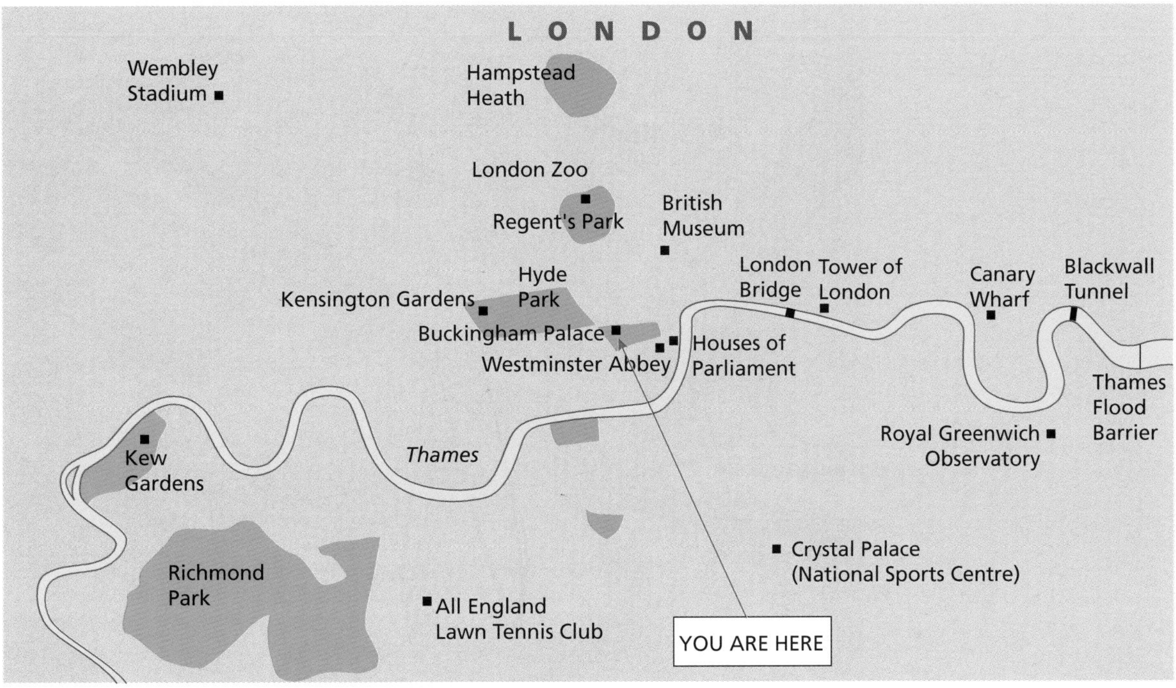

a) London Zoo is roughly __________.

b) London Bridge is roughly __________.

c) Kew Gardens is roughly __________.

d) The All England Lawn Tennis Club is roughly __________.

What direction are the following (NW, SW, NE or SE)?

e) The British Museum is roughly __________.

f) Richmond Park is roughly __________.

g) Wembley Stadium is roughly __________.

11 Some people give directions as parts of a clock in hours.

If you were at Buckingham Palace, the British Museum would be at '1 o'clock'.

From Buckingham Palace, which places are roughly at:

a) 3 o'clock? b) 7 o'clock? c) 10 o'clock?

12 Look at the street map from a London A–Z below.

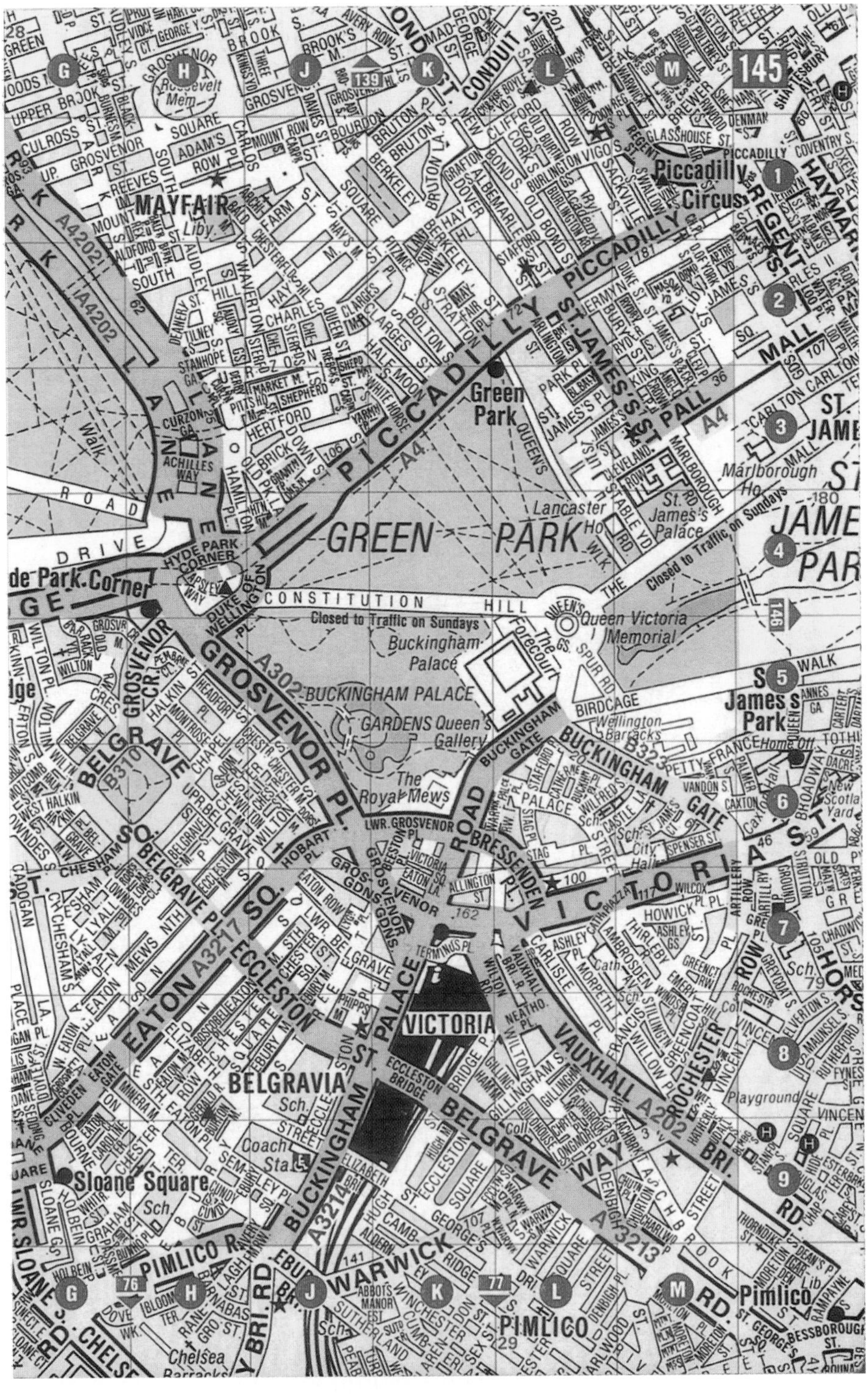

To find a place, the index gives the name, page and reference for the square the place is in.

Piccadilly Circus is in square M1.

a) Which Station is in K8?

b) Which Park covers J4, K4 and L4?

c) Which Square is in G9?

d) Which Corner is in H4?

13 Now try Worksheet 5 *Find the place.*

14 Give directions (names of streets) to go from:
(Remember you can use left, right and compass directions as well as street names.)

a) the Queen Victoria Memorial (L5) to Piccadilly Circus (M1)

b) Green Park Station (● in L3) to Mayfair Post Office (★ in H1)

c) St James's Palace (M4) to Hyde Park Corner (H4)

d) Hyde Park Corner (H4) to Mayfair Post Office (★ in H1)

15 Try Worksheet 6 *Street angles.*

TEST TIME

Now try Unit 4 Test.

Review 4

1 What is the **value** of the **5** in each of these numbers? Write each in **digits** and **words**.

millions **hundreds of thousands** **tens of thousands** **thousands** **hundreds** **tens** **units**

a) 6546 b) 5 363 420 c) 456

d) 25 684 e) 65 f) 50 483

2 Fill in the missing numbers.

a)

×	2	3	4	5	10
7		21			
8		24		40	
6	12				60

b)

×	6	10	7	8	9
4		40			
8			56		72
6	36				

Ken buys six books. How much would he pay for one if the bill came to:

c) £48? d) £54? e) £60?

f) £24? g) £18?

3 Find a **half** or **50%** of these amounts:

a) 8 cm b) 14 kg c) 2 litres d) £400

Find a **quarter** or **25%** of these amounts:

e) £36 f) 2 litres g) £400 h) £4000

Find a **tenth** or **10%** of these amounts:

i) 80 cm j) 100 km k) £400 l) 60 litres

4 Write how you would **say** these times – approximately.

a) 

b) 

c) 

d) 

5 a) Find the area and the perimeter of this rectangle.

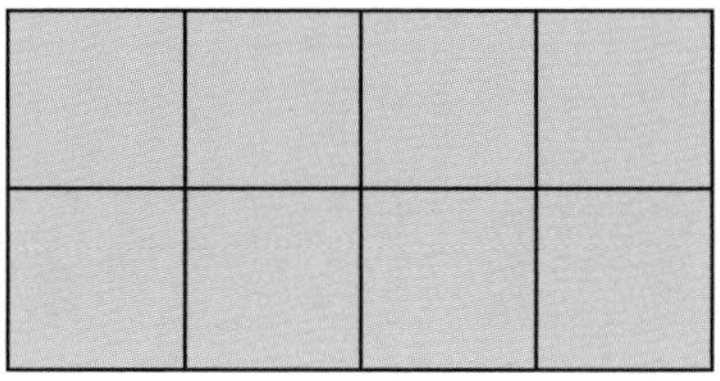

b) A room measures **4 metres** wide and **8 metres** long. Which of these carpets would fit it with some left over?

A 4 square metres
B 12 square metres
C 40 square metres

5 Number

Fractions, decimals and percentages

Unit 5 words

survey	**interest**	tenth
hundredth	fraction	percentage
decimal point	cost	figures
amounts	half	chance

Remember

Examples are shown in red.

means copy and complete.

You need

- a set of Unit 5 vocabulary Snap cards.

Play a game of Snap to help you learn the words.

Try the **word test** to get some points.

1 In this block **one hundredth** (**1** out of **100**) is shaded.

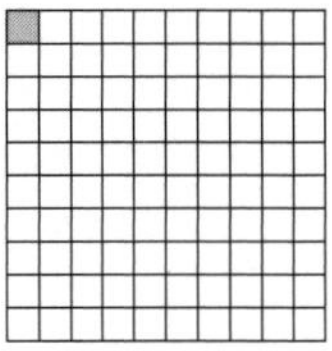

one out of a hundred $= \frac{1}{100}$ (one hundredth) or 1%

Write the shaded parts of these blocks as a **fraction** and as a **percentage**.

Remember	Remember	Remember
10% is the same as $\frac{1}{10}$ To find $\frac{1}{10}$, we ÷10	**50%** is the same as $\frac{1}{2}$ To find $\frac{1}{2}$, we ÷2	**25%** is the same as $\frac{1}{4}$ To find $\frac{1}{4}$, we ÷4

a) 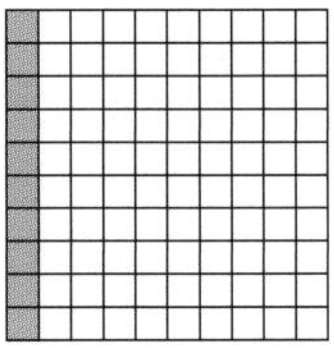

b) 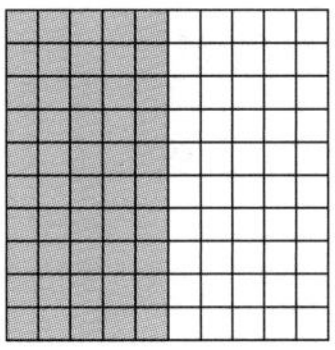

c) 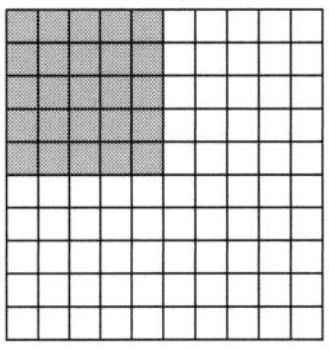

2 How many parts would you need to shade for:

a) 100%?

b) 0%?

3 Now try Worksheet 1 *Percentage workout.*

Remember

100p = £1

4 What percentage of a pound (£1) are these amounts?

a) 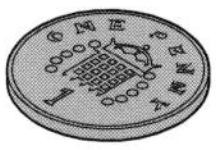

b) 

c) 

d) 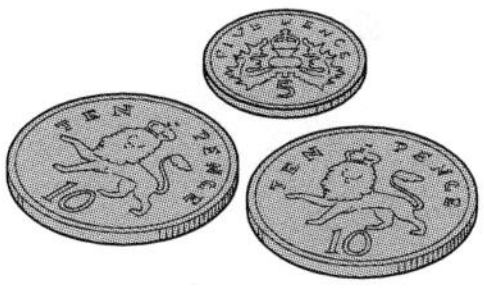

5 Use the £ sign and the decimal point to write the following amounts as decimals:

a) **fifty**  coins

b) **five**  coins

c) **one**  coin

d) What do you notice about the answers above?

6 Write as **fractions** and as **decimals**:

a) one hundredth $= \frac{1}{100}$ or 0.01

b) ten hundredths

c) twelve hundredths

d) nineteen hundredths

e) twenty hundredths

f) twenty-five hundredths

g) fifty hundredths

h) one tenth

i) one tenth and two hundredths

j) one tenth and nine hundredths

k) two tenths

l) two tenths and five hundredths

m) five tenths

7 Write the shaded parts as a **fraction**, as a **decimal** and as a **percentage**.

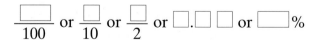

a)

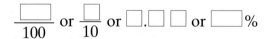

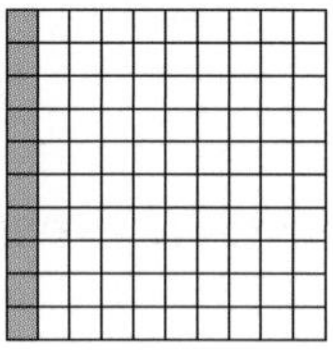

$\frac{\square}{100}$ or $\frac{\square}{10}$ or $\square.\square\,\square$ or $\square$%

b)

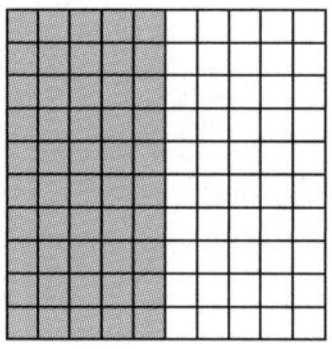

$\frac{\square}{100}$ or $\frac{\square}{10}$ or $\frac{\square}{2}$ or $\square.\square\,\square$ or $\square$%

c) 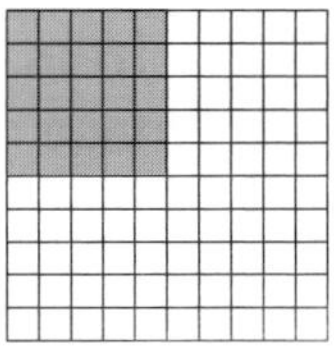

$\frac{\square}{100}$ or $\frac{\square}{4}$ or $\square.\square\,\square$ or $\square$%

d) 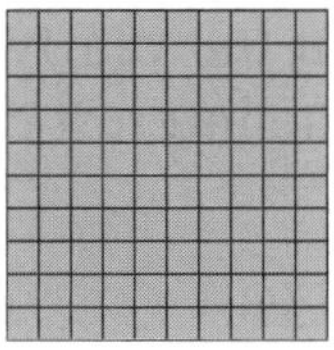

$\frac{\square}{100}$ or $\square.\square\,\square$ or $\square$%

8 a) 50% + 50% = $\square$%

b) 70% + $\square$% = 100%

c) 100% − 20% = $\square$%

d) 100% − $\square$% = 90%

e) $\square$% − 1% = 99%

f) 40% + 20% + $\square$% = 100%

9 Try Worksheet 2 *Add and subtract fractions, decimals and percentages.*

10 When you save money in a bank you get a **fraction** or a **percentage** of the amount saved added on.

> **Remember**
>
> When **saving**, the percentage added on is called the **interest earned**.

> **Remember**
>
> **10%** is the same as $\frac{1}{10}$
> To find $\frac{1}{10}$, we ÷10

If a bank worked out the yearly interest of 10% on people's savings, what would the interest earned be on each of these savings?

a) £30 b) £300 c) £3000 d) £90

e) £900 f) £60 g) £640 h) £2700

i) £4000 j) £4850

11 When you borrow money from a bank you have to pay it back **plus** a **fraction** or a **percentage** of the amount borrowed.

> **Remember**
>
> When **borrowing**, the percentage added on is called the **interest charged**.

> **Remember**
>
> **25%** is the same as $\frac{1}{4}$
> To find $\frac{1}{4}$, we $\div 4$

If a bank worked out the yearly interest of 25% on people's loans, what would the interest charged be on each of these loans?

a) £36 b) £360 c) £4000 d) £80

e) £800 f) £60 g) £840 h) £8400

i) £280 j) £2800

12 Raj and Tara each want to buy a television which **costs £80**.

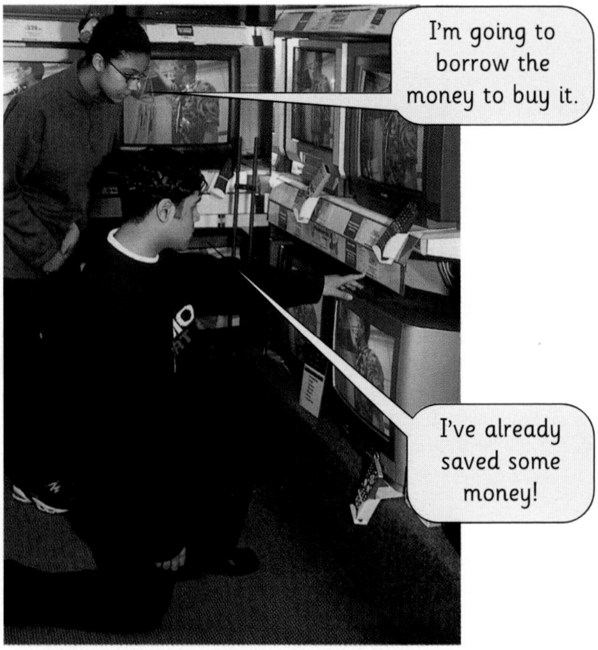

I'm going to borrow the money to buy it.
I've already saved some money!

> **Remember**
>
> If you **save** money to buy something, the **interest you gain** from saving will **help you pay** some of the cost.
>
> If you **borrow** money to buy something, the **interest you are charged** for borrowing will **add more to the cost**.

Raj has saved £80.
He gets **10%** interest on the **£80** he saved.

a) He gets £☐ interest.

b) After he pays for the television he still has £☐ left.

Tara takes out a loan.
She is charged **10%** yearly interest on the **£80** she borrows.

c) She will be charged £☐ interest.

d) With the interest she is charged added onto the price, the television will really cost her £☐.

e) How much more does Tara pay for the television than Raj?

13 What is the real amount to pay for the following things if the money is **saved** or **borrowed**?

Item	Amount needed	Rate of interest	Interest gained or charged	Real amount to pay after saving	Real amount to pay after borrowing	Difference in amounts
a) Trainers	£80	10%	£8	£80 − £8 = £72	£80 + £8 = £88	£16 (£88 − £72)
b) Jeans	£100	10%				
c) Stereo	£300	10%				
d) Holiday	£500	10%				
e) Bike	£1500	10%				
f) Car	£8000	10%				
g) House	£150 000	10%				

a) Interest gained or charged = £8

With interest saved trainers will really cost £72. (£80 − £8)

With interest charged trainers will really cost £88. (£80 + £8)

Difference in cost = £16

Find out if interest is:

h) higher when you save or when you borrow.

i) the same wherever you save or borrow.

j) For which of the items above would it be very hard for most people to save?

14 Work out these percentages.

10% of:	a) 20	b) 100	c) 10 000	d) 1 000 000
25% of:	e) 20	f) 100	g) 10 000	h) 1 000 000
50% of:	i) 20	j) 100	k) 10 000	l) 1 000 000

15 Schools look at attendance in different groups. Tom was asked to work out the group with best attendance. He tells his friend Jon his results.

What are the **most** absences possible in a week for:

a) Tom's group? b) Jon's group?

c) Why would it be unfair for Tom's group to win?

Think about:
Tom's group had **20** absences out of a possible total of **40**. (5×8)
$\frac{1}{2}$ or **50%** of Tom's group were absent.

Jon's group had **25** absences out of a possible total of **100**. (5×20)
$\frac{1}{4}$ or **25%** of Jon's group were absent.

d) Why do you think schools work out attendance in percentages (%)?

16 Look at the following claims made in advertising. Say why you think people should buy the products or not.

50% of young people wear Jite trainers

60% of all American adults own a car

95% of teenagers said they drank Tinger

80% of cats prefer Kattyfood

90% of owners of Tong cars said they would buy the same car again

Try to collect as many examples as you can of percentages used in advertising.

17 Here are the results of a survey of accidents in the home.

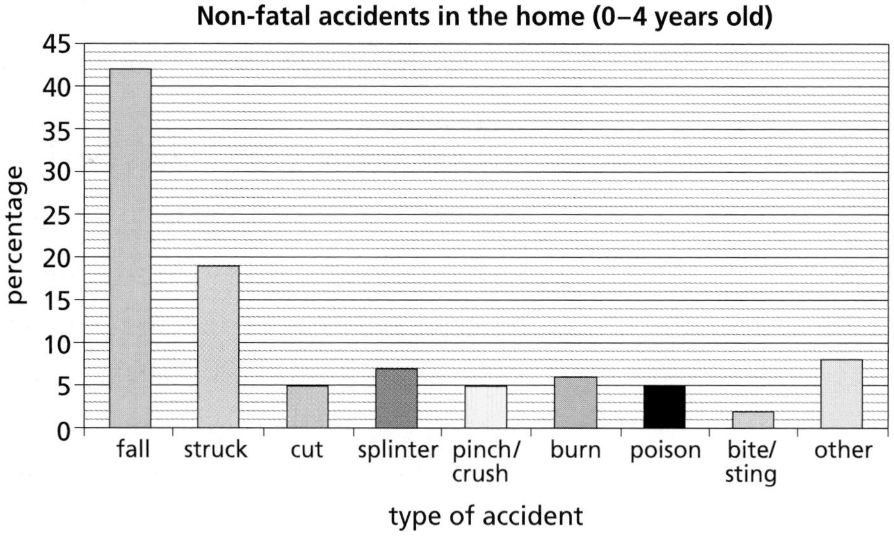

In this group (0–4 years):

a) ☐% were poisoned

b) ☐% were struck by something

c) ☐% were burned

d) 42% __________

True or **false**?

e) More than half the accidents are from falls.

f) There are less children burned than cut.

g) There are more children stung than poisoned.

h) Less than a tenth of the children get splinters.

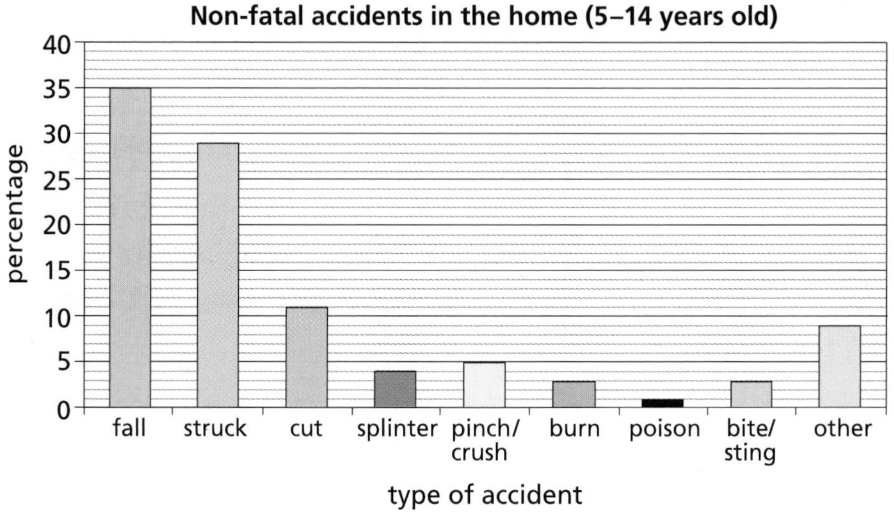

In the older group (5–14 years):

i) ☐% fell

j) ☐% were cut

k) ☐% were stung

l) 35% ________

True or **false**?

m) Less than half the accidents are from falls.

n) There are more children cut than burned.

o) More children are struck by something than fall.

p) Less than a quarter of the children fall.

Look at both of the accident survey graphs.

True or **false**?

q) More older children are struck than younger children.

r) Younger children fall more than older children.

s) Younger children accidentally take poison more often than older children.

t) More younger children than older children get bitten or stung.

What are the chances (very likely, likely, unlikely, very unlikely, impossible) of:

u) falling if you are two years old?

v) accidentally taking poison if you are twelve years old?

w) falling out of a window if you are ten years old?

x) being struck by something if you are three years old?

y) What sort of accidents do you think the 'other' accidents might be?

18 Try Worksheet Puzzle *One hundred hours.*

19 Try a game of **Around problems**.

TEST TIME

Now try Unit 5 Test.

Review 5

1 These are the sizes of girls' trousers sold in a shop in one month.

Size	Tallies	Frequency
8	𝍸	
10	𝍸 𝍸 𝍸	
12	𝍸 𝍸 𝍸 𝍸 𝍸 I	
14	𝍸 𝍸 𝍸 𝍸 𝍸 𝍸 𝍸 III	
16	𝍸 𝍸 𝍸 𝍸 II	
18	𝍸 𝍸 𝍸	

a) Fill in the frequency (the number of times) each trouser size was sold.

size 8, frequency is 5

b) What is the **mode** value?

c) What is the **median** value?

d) Are the mode and the median values the same?

2 What is the value of the bold digit:

millions, hundred thousands, ten thousands, thousands, hundreds, tens or **units?**

a) 10**4**2358 b) **1**942358

c) 642**3**58 d) 1**8**42350 e) 435**2**

3 Tina paid £2160 for a car. She paid £1938 for a holiday.

a) How much did she pay for both?

b) How much more did she pay for her car than for her holiday?

4 Look at the train timetable from Leeg to Crag below.

Station	Departs
Leeg	6.50 a.m.
Randel	7.00 a.m.
Bentley	7.30 a.m.
Siner	7.45 a.m.
Crag	8.15 a.m.

What time does the train leave:

a) Leeg? b) Bentley? c) Randel? d) Siner?

How long does the journey take from:

e) Randel to Siner? f) Siner to Crag? g) Leeg to Crag?

6 Shape and space

Circles

Unit 6 words

circumference	**radius**	**radii**
diameter	**rotate**	**centre**
cone	**sector**	**pair of compasses**
forward	cylinder	size

Remember

Examples are shown in red.

means copy and complete.

You need

- a set of Unit 6 vocabulary Snap cards.

Play a game of Snap to help you learn the words.

Try the **word test** to get some points.

1 

a) What do you think the circles on the Olympic flag stand for?

b) Why do you think this symbol is chosen?

2 You need

- a calculator.

Wheels are **circle shaped**.
They turn easily so can carry heavy loads or move quickly.

Remember

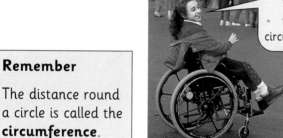

The distance round a circle is called the **circumference**.

The wheels on my wheelchair have a circumference of 160 cm.

Toni

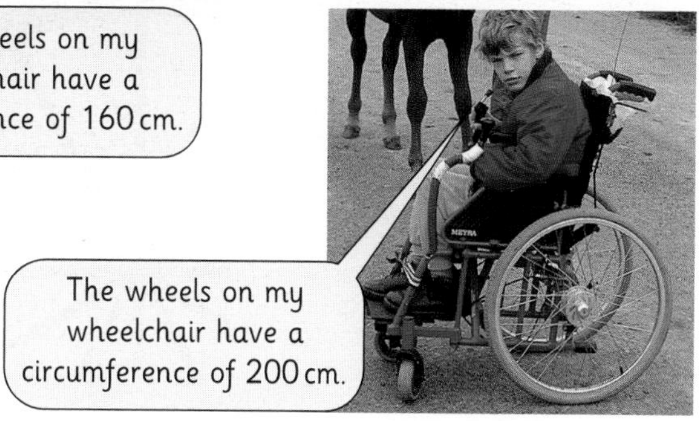

The wheels on my wheelchair have a circumference of 200 cm.

Mike

Mike pushes his wheels around 5 times.
Toni pushes her wheels around 6 times.

a) Who covers the longest distance?

b) Write both distances in metres and centimetres.

Mike pushes his wheels around 7 times.
Toni pushes her wheels around 9 times.

c) Who covers the longest distance?

d) Write both distances in centimetres and metres.

Mike pushes his wheels around 8 times.
Toni pushes her wheels around 10 times.

e) Who covers the longest distance?

f) Write both distances in centimetres and metres.

How many times would they each push their wheels round if:

g) Toni moves forward 2000 cm?

h) Mike moves forward 2400 cm?

3 You need

- a ruler.

Remember

The distance from the **centre** of a circle to the **circumference** is called the **radius**.

A spoke on a wheel is a **radius**.
Measure the length of the radius in each of these circles.

a)

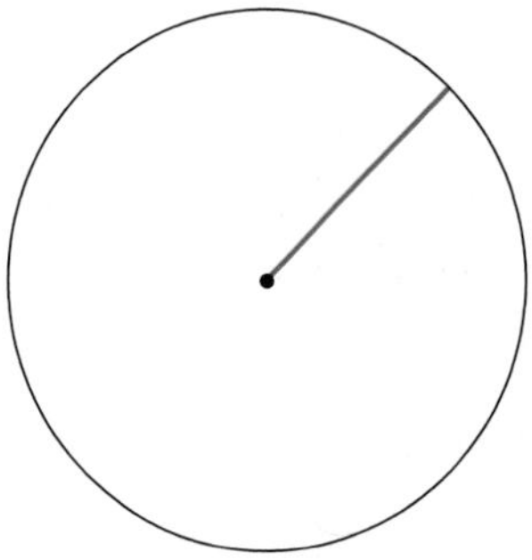

b)

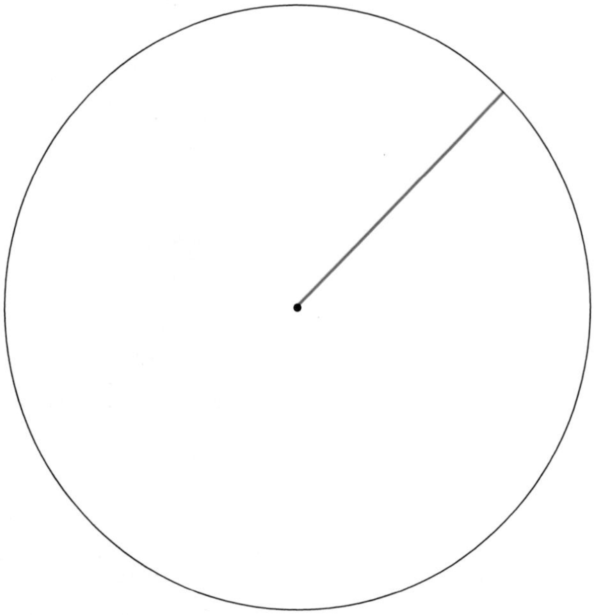

c)

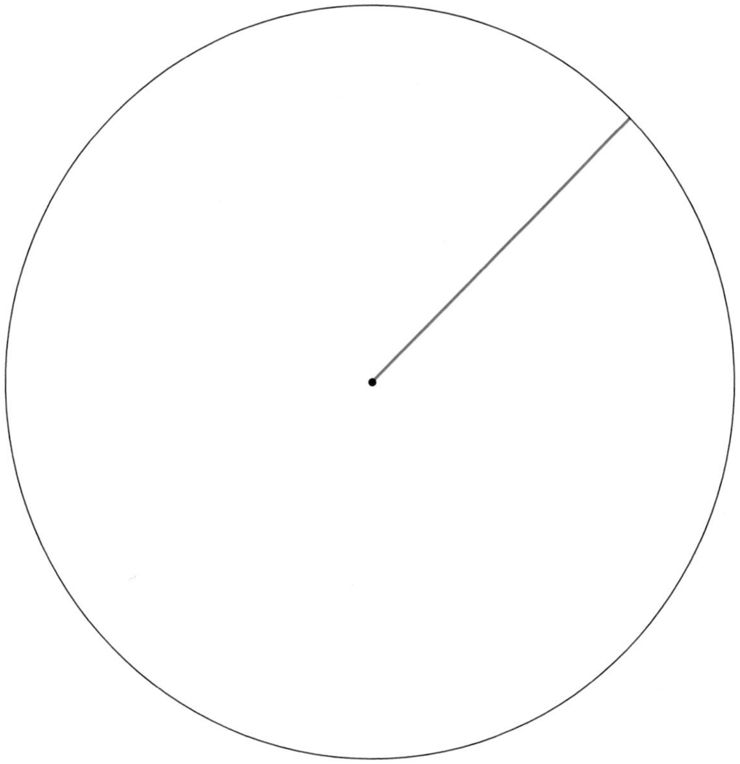

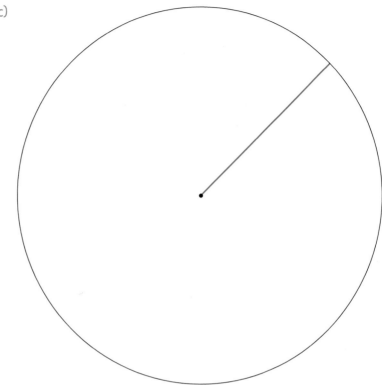

4 You need

- a pair of compasses for drawing circles
- a ruler.

Draw some circles each with a different radius.
The drawings below show you how to mark off a radius and draw a circle with a radius of 2 cm.

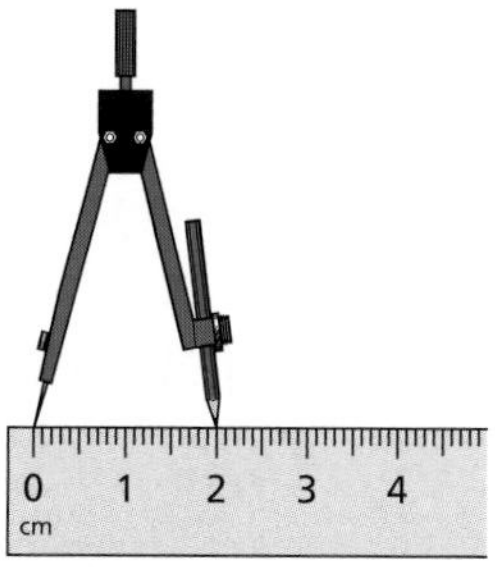

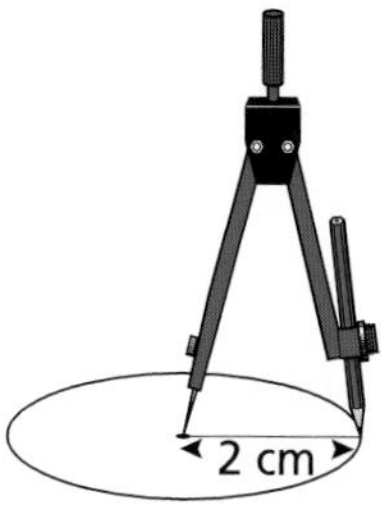

Remember to start at the correct place on your ruler.

Remember to keep the point fixed and rotate the pencil.

Draw circles with a radius of:

a) 3 cm b) 5 cm c) 4 cm d) 6 cm

5 Now try Worksheet 1 *Circles in a square.*

6 You need

- a pair of compasses
- a ruler.

Draw a **bull's eye** like this:

a) Draw a circle with a radius of 5 cm.

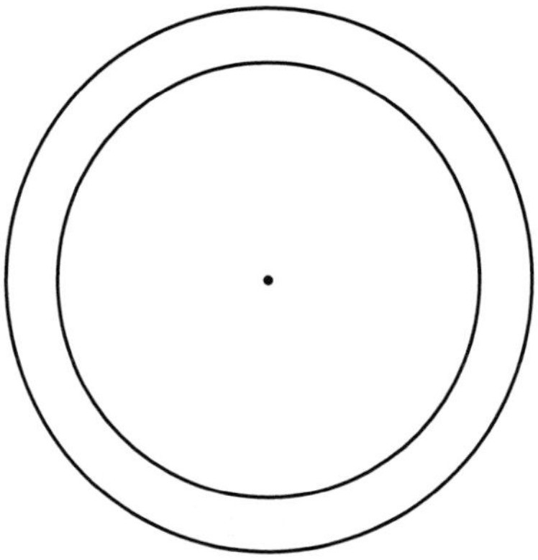

b) Put the point of your compass *on the same centre* and draw another circle with a radius of 4 cm.

c) Put the point of your compass *on the same centre* and draw another circle with a radius of 3 cm.

d) Put the point of your compass *on the same centre* and draw another circle with a radius of 2 cm.

e) Colour each band a different colour.

f) Draw some more bull's eyes of your own, each with different radii.

7 Now try Worksheets 2 and 3 *Measure a diameter (1)* and *(2)*.

Remember

The distance across a circle – from one side of the circumference to the other – going through the centre is called the **diameter**.

8 Find the diameter of a circle if its radius is:

a) 2 cm b) 10 cm c) 2.5 cm

d) 50 cm e) 15 cm f) 8 cm

9 Find the radius of a circle if its diameter is:

a) 12 cm b) 100 cm c) 10 cm

d) 11 cm e) 150 cm f) 80 cm

> **Remember**
>
> Keep your compasses at the same setting for parts a) to e).

10 Try this design.

a) Set your compasses to 4 cm and draw a circle with a radius of 4 cm and mark the centre.

b) Choose a point on the circumference and mark it U.

c) Place the point of your compasses on the point U and draw part of the circle around the new centre U like this:

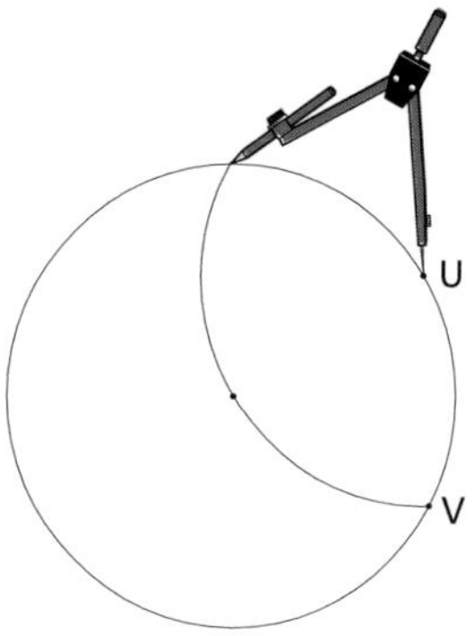

d) Now use the point V as the centre and draw another part of a circle like this:

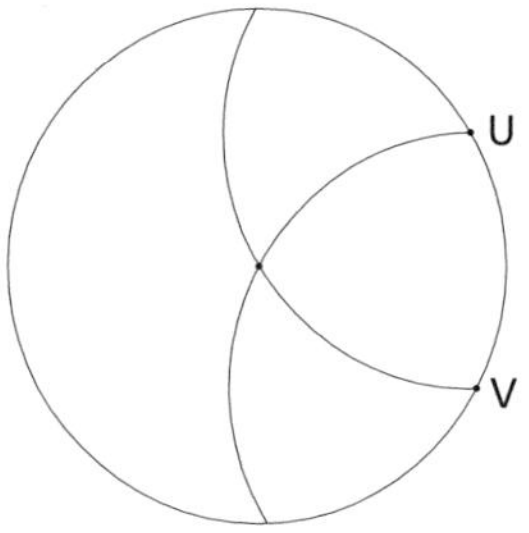

e) Continue with the new points until you make a pattern like this.

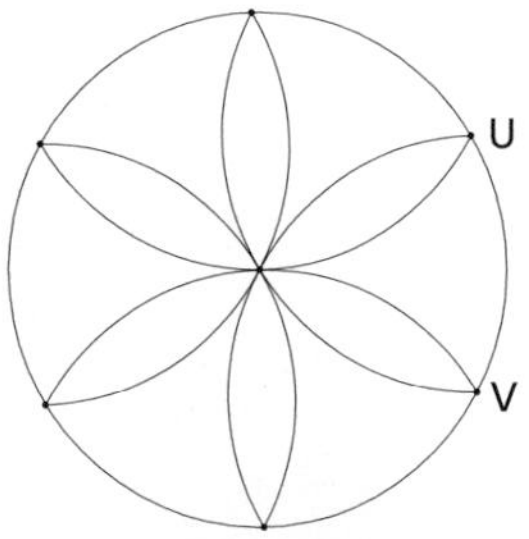

f) How many times could the finished shape be turned around and still fit exactly on itself?
You can use tracing paper to help you find out.

g) Try drawing this pattern with circles of different sizes.

11 Now try Worksheet 4 *Percentage circle*.

12 These things are **cone shaped**.

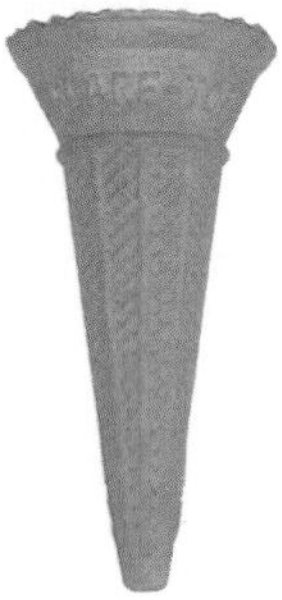

Why do you think they are made in this shape?

13 Now try Worksheet 5 *Make a cone*.

14 These cones are made from the same circle with a part cut out.

A **B** **C** **D**

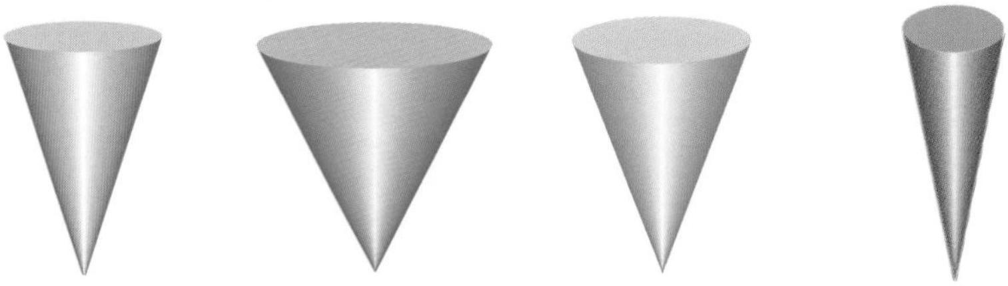

a) Which cone has the largest **part** or **sector** cut out?

b) Which cone has the smallest **part** or **sector** cut out?

15 These things are made in the shape of a **cylinder**.

Why do you think they are made in this shape?

16 Which rectangle will fit with which circle to make a cylinder?

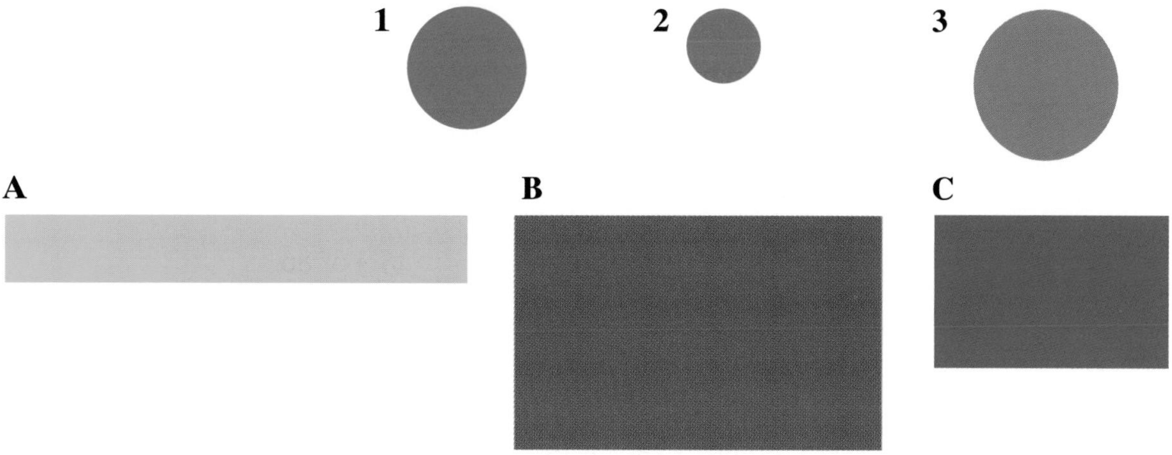

17 Now try Worksheets 6, 7 and 8 *Circle links (1), (2)* and *(3)*.

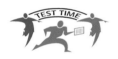

Now try Unit 6 Test.

Review 6

1 Write as 24-hour times:

a) 1.20 p.m. b) 8.05 a.m. c) 9.15 p.m.

Write as 12-hour times:

d) 12:20 e) 09:05 f) 22:55

2 a) $45 \div 5$ b) $\frac{1}{2}$ of 86

c) $27 \div 3$ d) $\frac{1}{4}$ of 168

e) $300 \div 6$

3 A club hires vans for a trip out.
Each van will take 8 people.
How many vans will it take each time and how many seats will be left empty if:

a) 64 people go? b) 29 people go?

c) 21 people go? d) 72 people go?

How many people went if they used:

e) 4 full vans?

f) 5 vans with 3 empty seats?

g) 9 vans with 4 empty seats?

4 If  stands for 1000 letters, what do the following stand for?

a) 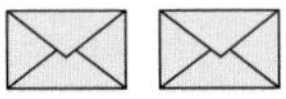 b) 

c) 

d) 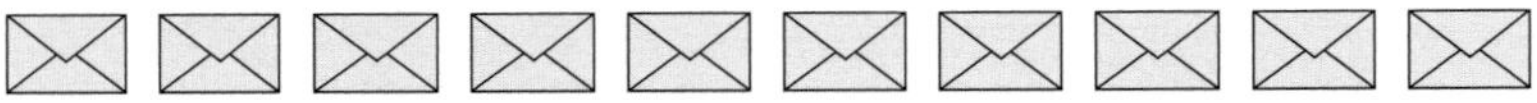

5 Write the shaded parts of these blocks as decimals.

a)

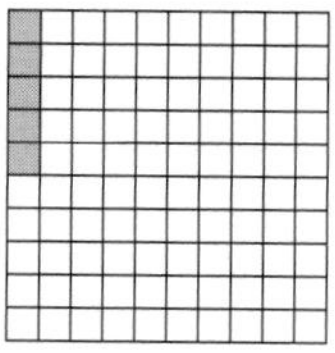

□.□ □

b)

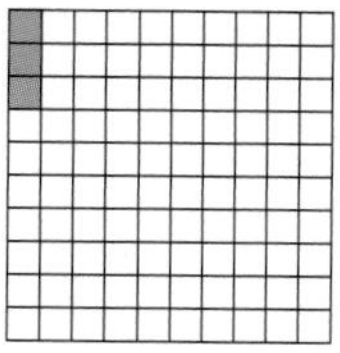

□.□ □

c)

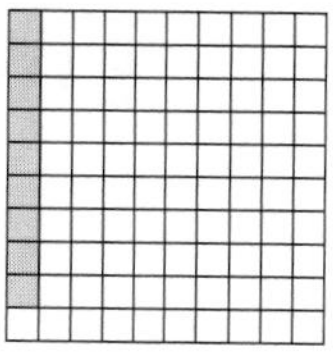

□.□ □

d)

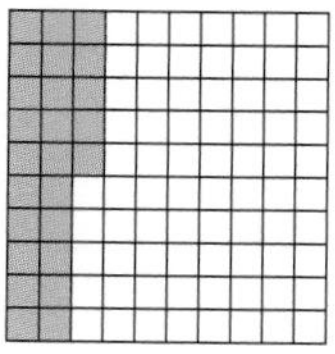

□.□ □

6 Write the correct size of each angle.

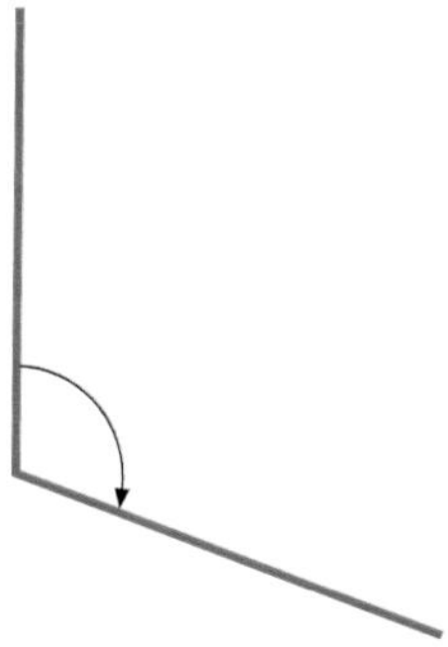

a) 80°, 110° or 170°?

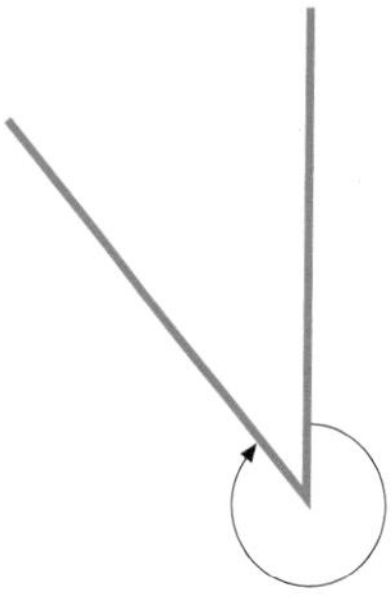

b) 40°, 220° or 320°?

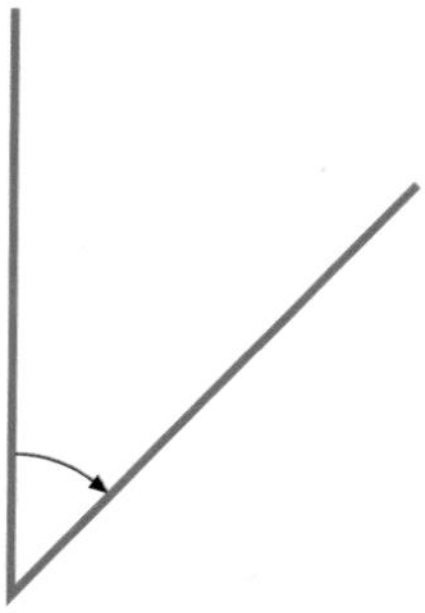

c) 20°, 45° or 95°?

7 Measures

Time

Unit 7 words

local time	**later**	**earlier**
noon	**behind**	**arrival**
departure	days	minutes
afternoon	forward	timetable

Remember

Examples are shown in red.

means copy and complete.

You need

- a set of Unit 7 vocabulary Snap cards.

Play a game of Snap to help you learn the words.

Try the **word test** to get some points.

1 Emma's birthday is on January 10th. In 2002 she will be 16 years old.

a) Emma was born in the year ______.

b) She will be 21 years old in the year ______.

c) She will be 30 years old in the year ______.

d) In 2026 she will be ______ years old.

e) In 2086 she will be ______ years old.

2

○ JANUARY 2002 ○					
Sun		6	13	20	27
Mon		7	14	21	28
Tues	1	8	15	22	29
Wed	2	9	16	23	30
Thurs	3	⑩	17	24	31
Fri	4	11	18	25	
Sat	5	12	19	26	

The day:

a) of Emma's sixteenth birthday, the 10th of January, will be a _____.

b) seven days before will be a _____.

c) two weeks after will be a _____.

d) The first day of the month will be a _____.

e) The last day of the month will be a _____.

f) The first day of February will be a _____.

The date:

g) seven days before Emma's birthday is _____.

h) of the last Saturday in January is _____.

i) of the third Monday in January is _____.

You may use a calculator.

On the 17th of January, Emma will be 16 years old **and**:

j) ☐ week k) ☐ days l) ☐ hours

m) ☐ minutes n) ☐ seconds

3 Now try Worksheet 1 *Changing times*.

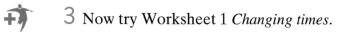

4 If the time is 4.30 p.m., what is the time:

a) 25 minutes later?
b) 25 minutes earlier?
c) 45 minutes later?
d) 45 minutes earlier?
e) 1 hour and 20 minutes later?
f) 1 hour and 20 minutes earlier?
g) 3 hours and 30 minutes later?
h) 3 hours and 30 minutes earlier?

5 How many hours or hours and minutes have passed from:

a) 08:20 to 08:45?
b) 04:22 to 04:32?
c) 08:35 to 09:00?
d) 05:04 to 05:34?
e) 01:30 to 14:30?
f) 01:20 to 16:00?
g) 19:45 to 20:00?
h) 19:50 to 22:00?
i) 19:50 to 22:10?

6 Emma's friends plan to give a party for her close friends. They meet to plan a menu.
These are the menus they each suggest and the times they will take to cook.

a) Sue

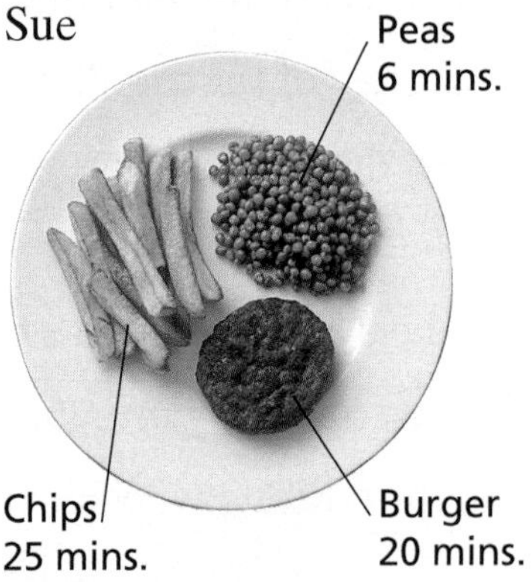

b) Sanjay

c) Pat

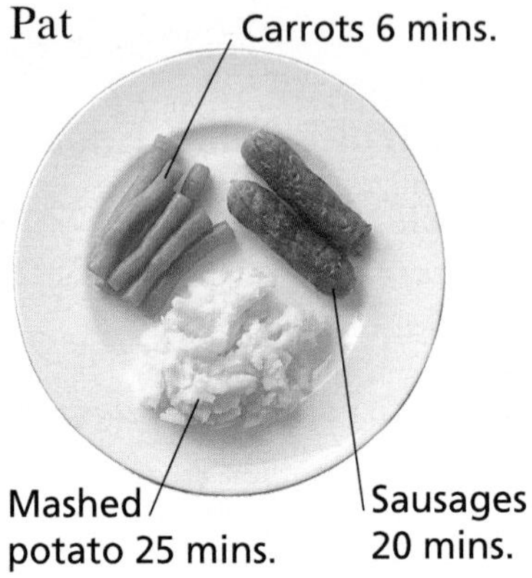

d) Jack

They want to have the meal ready for 7.30 p.m.
Write a plan for **each** meal.

You may use Worksheet 2 *Timelines* to help you.
Show the time each item will have to start cooking like this:

Sue's meal

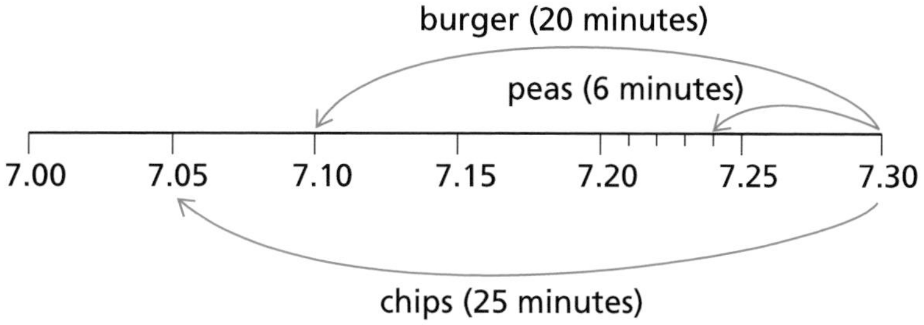

e) Why do you think the arrows are pointing back from the finishing time?

7 Now try Worksheet 3 *Plan more meals*.

8 Emma's friends decide to cook chicken, baked potato and a mixture of vegetables.

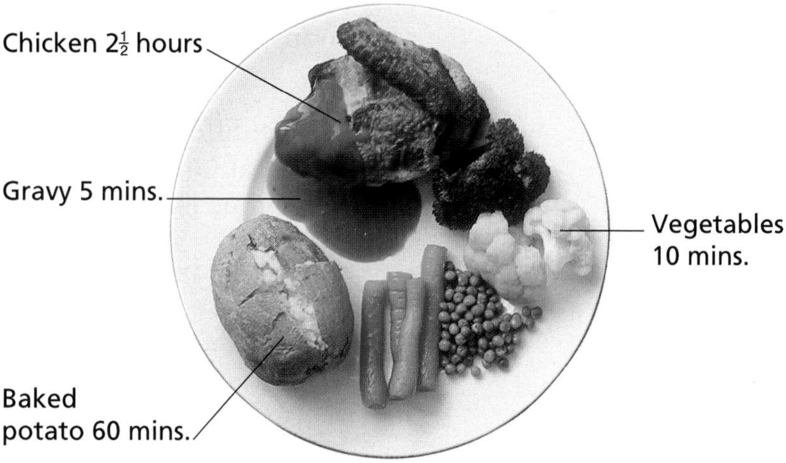

a) Put the foods in order of cooking time, longest first.

What time do you need to start cooking each food item if the meal is to be ready for:

b) 7.30 p.m.? c) 7.15 p.m.? d) 8.00 p.m.? e) 7.45 p.m.?

9 Copy the table and fill in the gaps.

In words	24-hour	a.m./p.m.
four o'clock in the afternoon	16:00	4.00 p.m.
		4.30 a.m.
	09:25	
quarter to ten in the morning		
	18:30	
five minutes to eleven at night		
		11.50 a.m.
twenty past twelve in the afternoon		

10 Put these eight times in order – **earliest** time first.

7.55 a.m.

19 : 55

quarter to eight in the morning

20:50

08 : 10

ten past three in the afternoon

10.36 p.m.

11 The sun rises at different times in different places.
It was agreed that Greenwich in London, would be the place from which all time is taken.

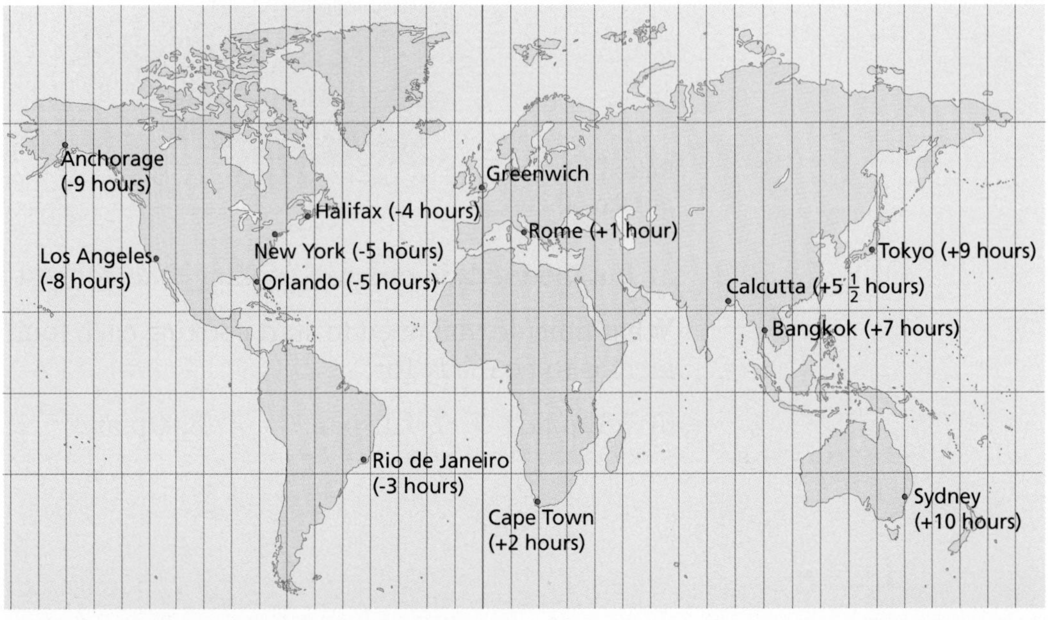

When it is 12:00 noon in London:

the local time is (+9 hours) in Tokyo.
(It is 9.00 p.m. or 21:00 hours.)

the local time is (−5 hours) in Orlando.
(It is 7.00 a.m. or 07:00 hours.)

If it is a Monday in January in London and the time is 5.00 p.m., what will the local time be in:

a) Rome? b) Sydney? c) Tokyo?
d) Cape Town? e) Bangkok? f) Calcutta?

If it is a Monday in January in London and the time is 6.00 a.m., what will the local time be in:

g) New York? h) Los Angeles? i) Orlando?
j) Rio de Janeiro? k) Anchorage? l) Halifax?

If it is a Monday in June in London and the time is 6.00 a.m., what will the local times be in the cities a)–l) above?

Remember

British Summer Time (BST) is one hour forward, from the end of March to the end of October. Be careful!

12 Emma has a lot of friends who live in different places around the world.
If they all want to ring her to wish her happy birthday at 8.00 a.m. on January 10th in London, what will their local time be in:

a) New York? b) Calcutta? c) Halifax?
d) Rome? e) Orlando? f) Sydney?

13 Now try Worksheet 4 *Journey times.*

14 Emma has friends in other parts of Britain who need to travel a long way to come to her party.

Use the timetables below.

Train
Manchester to London

Departs	Arrives
11:30	14:30
12:30	15:15
13:30	16:30
14:30	17:15
16:30	19:30
17:30	20:30
18:30	21:30
19:19	22:19
19:59	22:59

Train
Glasgow to London

Departs	Arrives
12:00	17:30
13:00	18:30
13:40	19:10
14:00	19:40
15:00	20:30
15:30	21:10
16:00	21:30
17:00	22:30

Bus
Cardiff to London

Departs	Arrives
09:00	12:30
11:00	14:30
12:30	16:00
12:45	19:30
15:00	20:30
15:30	21:00
15:45	21:30
18:00	22:30

Plane
Belfast to London

Departs	Arrives
07:00	08:30
10:30	11:50
13:00	14:10
15:00	16:10
17:05	18:15
19:05	20:25
21:10	22:15

What is the arrival time in London for:

a) the 16:30 train from Manchester?

b) the 15:00 train from Glasgow?

c) the 12:45 bus from Cardiff?

d) the 10:30 plane from Belfast?

How long would you have to wait for the next departure if you missed:

e) the 07:00 plane from Belfast?

f) the 12:45 bus from Cardiff?

g) the 14:30 train from Manchester?

h) the 15:00 train from Glasgow?

Emma's party is at 7.00 p.m.
Her friends need 30 minutes to get from the airport or station to Emma's house.

i) What is the time of the last bus, train or plane each can take to arrive on time?

TEST TIME

Now try Unit 7 Test.

Review 7

1 Write the balance **before** each of these withdrawals.

a)

Hartleys Bank

CURRENT ACCOUNT No: A

LOCATION: 08-08-08
WEST RD LONDON

WITHDRAWAL: £500 000.00

ACCOUNT BALANCE:
£500 000.00

THANK YOU

b)

Hartleys Bank

CURRENT ACCOUNT No: B

LOCATION: 03-03-03
ISLIP RD LONDON

WITHDRAWAL: £1500.00

ACCOUNT BALANCE:
£-1500.00

THANK YOU

Add the **even** numbers in each list together to find the total.

c) 10 84 17 402 193

d) 1100 363 2145 3900 15 437

2 How many hours do the following stand for?

Key:  = 2 hours.

a) 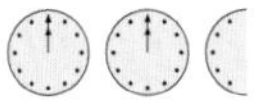

b) 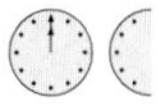

c) 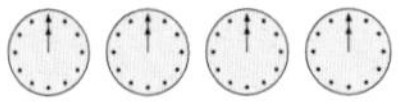

d) 

e) 

f) 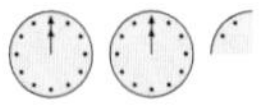

3 a) Put these weights in order to find the **median** or **middle** values.

56 kg 108 kg 100 g 77 kg 84 kg 112 kg 73 kg

b) Put these amounts of liquid in order – **smallest** first.

20 ml 2 ml 1000 ml $\frac{1}{2}$ litre 1020 ml 1500 ml

Approximate these lengths to the **nearest metre**.

c) 1.56 m d) 3.07 m e) 8.97 m f) 7.50 m

g) 4.14 m

4 a) Raj added 1.79 m to a garden path which was already 6.85 m long. How long was his new garden path?

Write down the weights shown on these scales.

b) 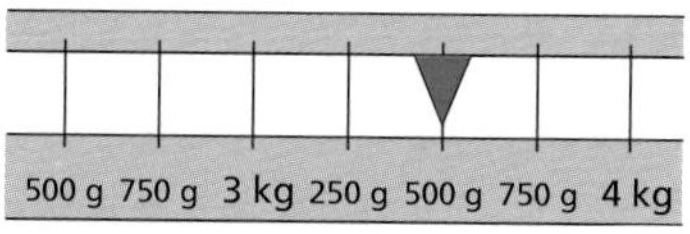

c) 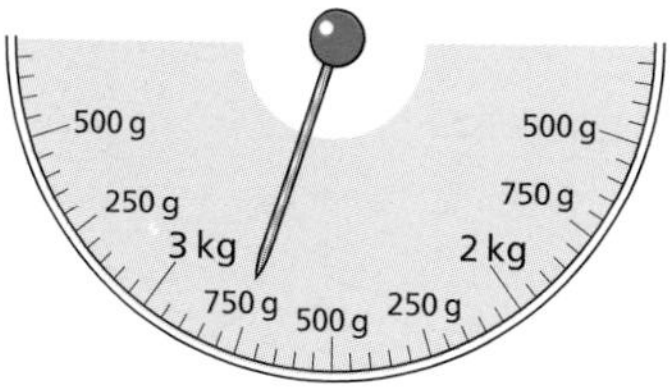

5 Find 10%, 25% and 50% of:

a) £20 b) £200 c) £2000

d) Write **four hundredths** as a fraction, a decimal and a percentage.

8 Measures

Mixed measures

Unit 8 words

depth	**unit of measure**	mile
height	metre (m)	millimetre (mm)
centimetre (cm)	kilometre (km)	kilogram (kg)
gram (g)	litre (l)	millilitre (ml)

Remember

Examples are shown in red.

means copy and complete.

You need

- a set of Unit 8 vocabulary Snap cards.

Play a game of Snap to help you learn the words.

Try the **word test** to get some points.

1 Write the name of something which measures:

a) 1 cm b) 30 cm c) 1 m

2 Which unit of measure,

millimetre (mm), centimetre (cm) or kilometre (km),

would you choose to measure:

a) the distance from London to Glasgow?

b) a pin head?

c) the length of your book?

> **Remember**
>
> The decimal point separates:
>
> the **pounds** from the **pence** and the **metres** from the **centimetres**.

3 Write in **decimals** as pounds (£):

a) 100p b) 150p c) 146p d) 34p

e) 10p f) 4p g) 1p

Write in **decimals** as metres (m):

h) 100 cm i) 150 cm j) 146 cm k) 34 cm

l) 10 cm m) 4 cm n) 1 cm

o) In what way are **pounds (£)** and **pence (p)** like **metres (m)** and **centimetres (cm)**?

4 We always write decimal money with two places after the decimal point.

We write **140p** as **£1.40**.

When we write metres as decimals we sometimes write just one place after the decimal point.

We can write **140 cm** as **1.4 m**.

But we can also write it like money with two places after the decimal point.

We can also write **140 cm** as **1.40 m**.

Write these metres (m) as centimetres (cm).

a) 1.40 m b) 1.4 m c) 2.50 m d) 2.5 m

e) 0.30 m f) 0.3 m g) 0.03 m h) 0.9 m

i) 0.90 m j) 0.09 m

5 Write these centimetres (cm) as metres (m).

a) 120 cm b) 102 cm c) 240 cm d) 204 cm

e) 310 cm f) 301 cm g) 20 cm h) 2 cm

i) 80 cm j) 8 cm

6 Put these lengths in order – **smallest** length first.

a) 5 cm   83 cm   8 cm   10 cm   143 cm   19 cm

b) 5 m   93 m   24 m   136 m   14 m   2 m

c) 23 m 14 cm   2 m 10 cm   1 m 4 cm   50 m 1 cm   1 m 2 cm   20 m 20 cm

d) 50.10 m   3.02 m   2.30 m   16.46 m   3.20 m   16.64 m

7 Now try Worksheets 1 and 2 *Different ways (1)* and *(2)*.

8 Now try putting these lengths in order.
You will need to change the measures to the same unit – **centimetres** or **metres** – before you begin.

a) 142 cm   1.4 m   1.39 m   1 m 4 cm   1.24 cm

b) 3.20 cm   32 cm   2 m 30 cm   2 cm   2.03 m

9 Write these millimetres as metres.

a) 1000 mm   b) 1500 mm   c) 1050 mm   d) 1005 mm

Remember
1000 mm = 1 m

10 Write these lengths in columns.
Write the total in metres and millimetres.

a) 34 mm + 2000 mm + 2050 mm + 68 mm + 14 mm

b) 4 mm + 40 mm + 800 mm + 16 mm + 1000 mm

11 Noah moves into a new house.
He likes to cook for his friends.
He goes to a shop to plan a new kitchen.

Here are some of the things he can choose from.
The cupboards are called units and are measured in millimetres (mm). All the cupboards are the same height – 900 mm – and the same depth – 300 mm.

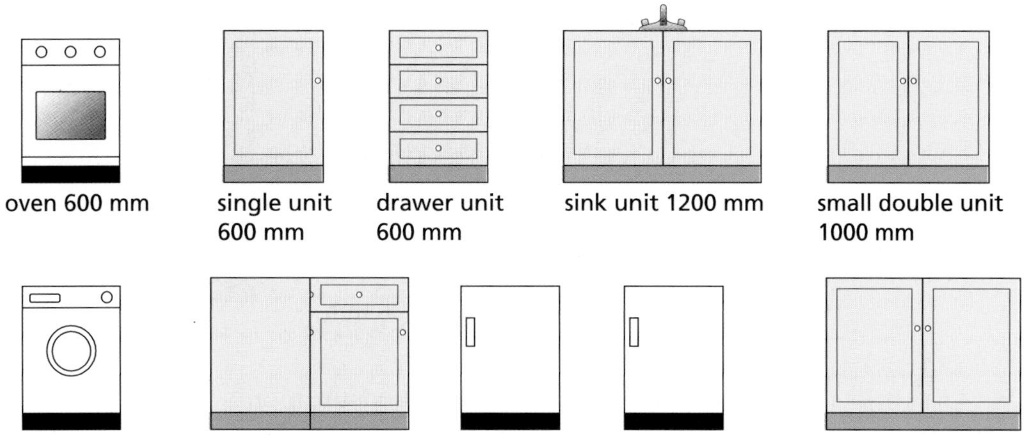

oven 600 mm

single unit 600 mm

drawer unit 600 mm

sink unit 1200 mm

small double unit 1000 mm

washing machine 600 mm

corner unit 1200 mm

fridge 600 mm

freezer 600 mm

double unit 1200 mm

a) Why do you think the cupboards are measured in millimetres (mm)?

b) Why do you think all the units are the same height and depth?

If you placed the fridge, the double unit and the freezer together with no spaces between them, you would fill up a wall which measures 2400 mm or 2 m 400 mm or 2.4 m.

c) If you placed two double units and a fridge together, they would take up

______ mm or ___ m ______ mm or ___.___ m.

d) If you placed two double units and a sink unit together, they would take up

______ mm or ___ m ______ mm or ___.___ m.

12 You can cut out and place pieces to help you choose the things Noah could fit into his kitchen.
Use Worksheets 3 and 4 *Plan a kitchen (1)* and *(2)*.

13 Noah needs curtains for the kitchen window.
The window measures 1200 mm long by 1200 mm wide.

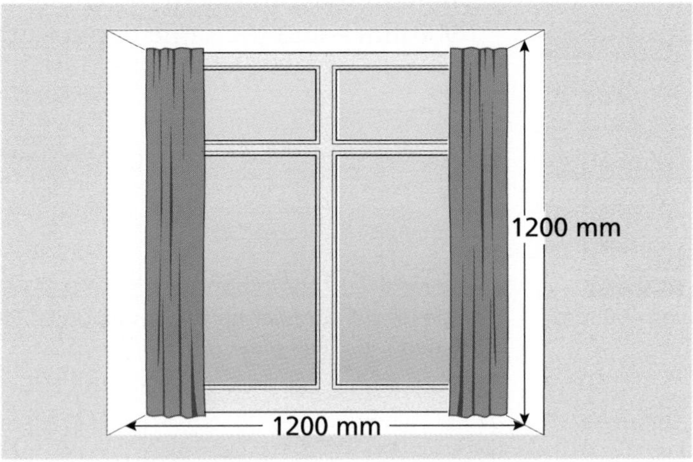

a) Write the window measurements in centimetres.

There is an extra 30 cm needed for the curtain hems.

b) How long will the fabric for each curtain length have to be?

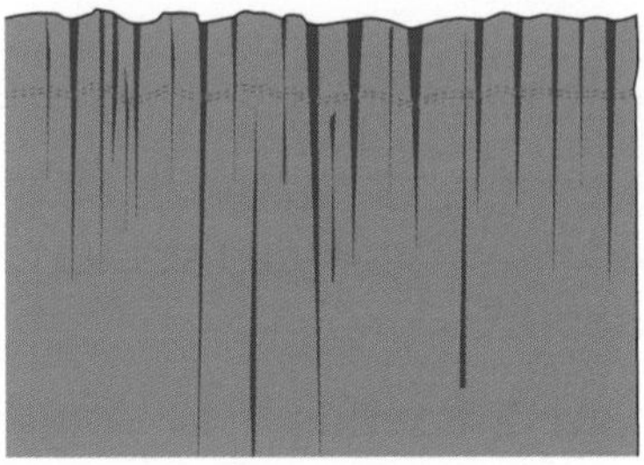

To make curtains with gathers, the width of the fabric needs to be twice the width of the window.
Noah wants to buy fabric which is 1.20 m wide.

c) How much would he have to buy for **one** curtain?

d) How much would he have to buy for **a pair** of curtains?

The fabric costs £4 a metre.

e) How much does he pay for the two curtains?

How much would he pay for a pair of curtains if the fabric costs:

f) £5 a metre?

g) £2.50 a metre?

14 a) There are [ ] metres in one kilometre (km).
In Britain we still measure long distances in **miles**.
In the rest of Europe they use **kilometres**.

Remember

A **mile** is just over **one and a half** times as long as a **kilometre**.
5 miles = 8 km.

b) Write down the missing kilometres.

miles		10		20		30		40		50
km	8		24		40		56		72	

Who travels further each time – Kim or Sue?

c) Kim travels 10 miles. Sue travels 8 km.

d) Kim travels 80 km. Sue travels 45 miles.

e) Kim travels $2\frac{1}{2}$ miles. Sue travels 4 km.

f) Kim travels 750 km. Sue travels 500 miles.

15 Now try Worksheet 5 *Post haste*.

16 Write the name of something which weighs about:

a) 1 gram (g)

b) 1000 g or 1 kilogram (kg)

17 Which unit of measure – **gram (g)** or **kilogram (kg)** – would you use to weigh:

a) a biscuit?

b) a car?

18 How many different ways could you use the weights below to balance:

a) $1\frac{1}{2}$ kg of sugar?

b) 3 kg of potatoes?

You can use as many of each weight as you wish.

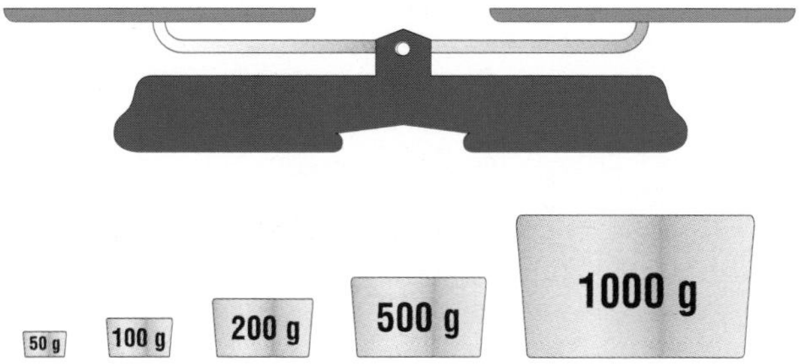

Remember

1000 g = 1 kg

19 Change the following quantities to kilograms.

a) 1500 g b) 500 g c) 1750 g
d) 2250 g e) 250 g f) 3250 g

Remember

$\frac{1}{2}$ kg = 500 g
$\frac{1}{4}$ kg = 250 g

20 Put these weights in order – **lightest** weight first.

a) $\frac{1}{2}$ kg 1500 g 250 g 1 kg 400 g 1 kg
b) 2450 g 2054 g 2 kg 50 g 2 kg 405 g 240 g
c) 1 kg 50 g 1600 g 50 g $\frac{1}{2}$ kg 1 kg
d) 240 g $4\frac{1}{4}$ kg $\frac{1}{4}$ kg 4 kg 500 g 750 g

21 Write these weights in columns.
Write the total in grams and kilograms.

a) 34 g + 245 g + 2 g + 689 g + 1004 g
b) 324 g + 204 g + 280 g + 6 g + 100 g
c) 401 g + 2 g + 180 g + 560 g + 1000 g

22 Work out the weights of parcels W, X, Y and Z from the following clues.

Parcel V

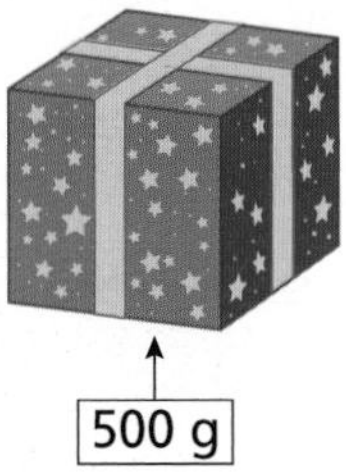

Parcel W

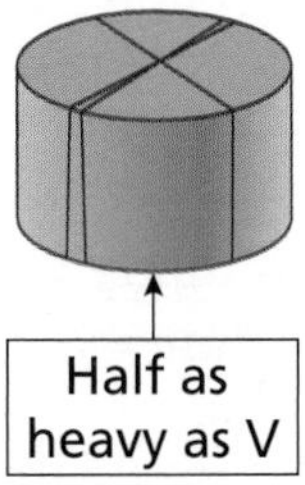

Parcel X

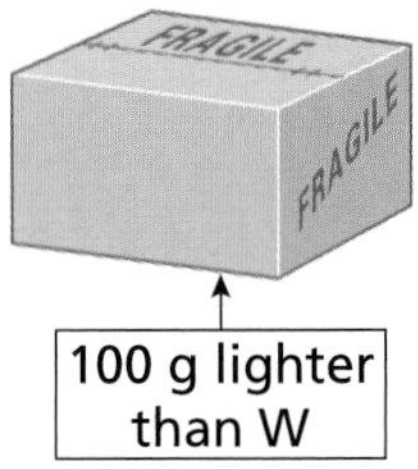

Parcel Y

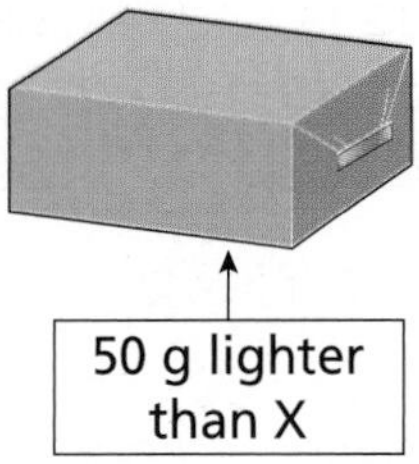

Parcel Z

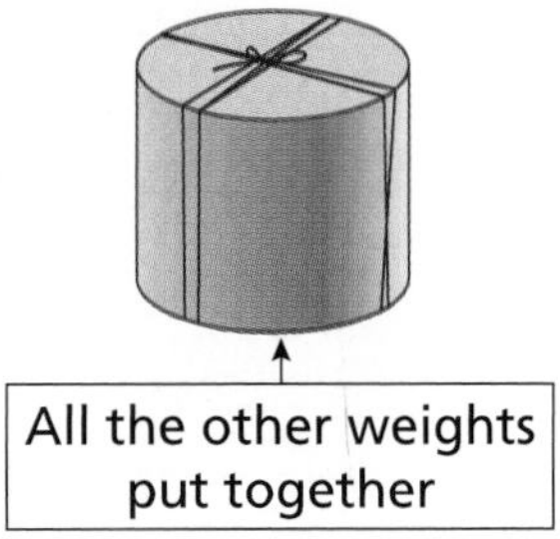

23 At the airport, bags are weighed before they can go on a plane. These people are going to Paris.

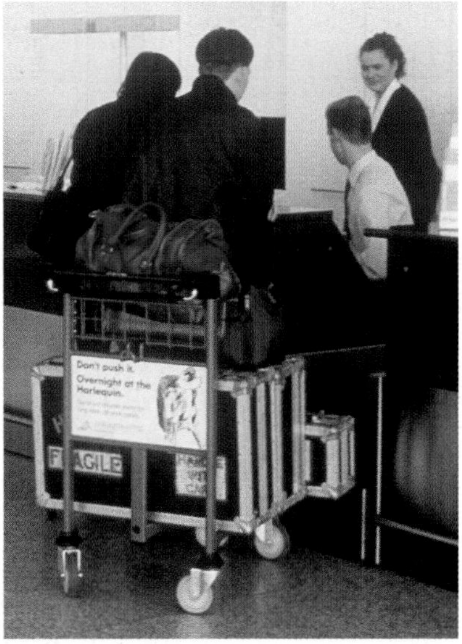

Each passenger is allowed to carry baggage weighing 23 kg. Read the following baggage weights and say if the passenger is carrying **over** or **under** or **exactly** the allowance.

a)

b)

c)

d)
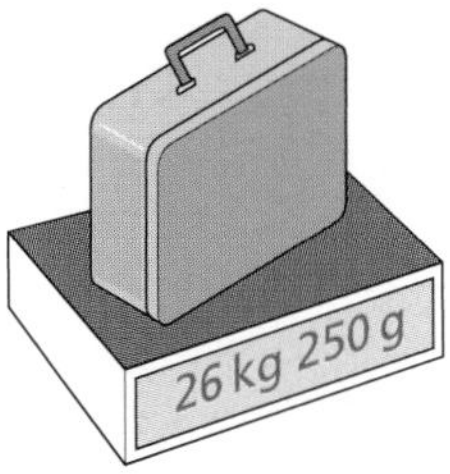

e)

f)

Passengers are charged £2 for each kilogram over the allowance.
How much would they pay if their baggage weighed:

g) 28 kg? h) 26 kg? i) 44 kg?

j) 31 kg? k) 52 kg? l) 63 kg?

24 Passengers going to America are allowed up to **two pieces** of luggage.
Each piece must weigh no more than 32 kg.
There is a charge of £3 for each kilogram overweight.
How much would each of these passengers be charged?

a) Wyatt had 2 cases weighing 38 kg and 30 kg.

b) Billy had 1 case weighing 42 kg.

c) Dolly had 2 cases weighing 45 kg and 37 kg.

d) Jesse had 2 cases weighing 32 kg and 47 kg.

e) Barbie had 1 case weighing 63 kg.

f) Buzz had 2 cases weighing 40 kg and 45 kg.

g) Woody had 2 cases weighing 33 kg and 63 kg.

h) If the passengers above were allowed a **total** of 64 kg instead of 32 kg per piece of luggage, how much would each have to pay?

25 Write the name of something which measures:

a) 1 litre (l) b) $\frac{1}{2}$l or 500 ml

Remember

1000 ml = 1 l

26 Write as litres (l):

a) 1000 ml b) 1500 ml c) 1050 ml d) 1005 ml

27 Which unit of measure – **litre (l)** or **millilitre (ml)** – would you choose to measure:

a) the water in a fish tank? b) a teaspoon of medicine?

c) the petrol in a car?

28 Sara likes to cook.
She measures liquid in a measuring jug.
How much liquid is in each jug?

a)

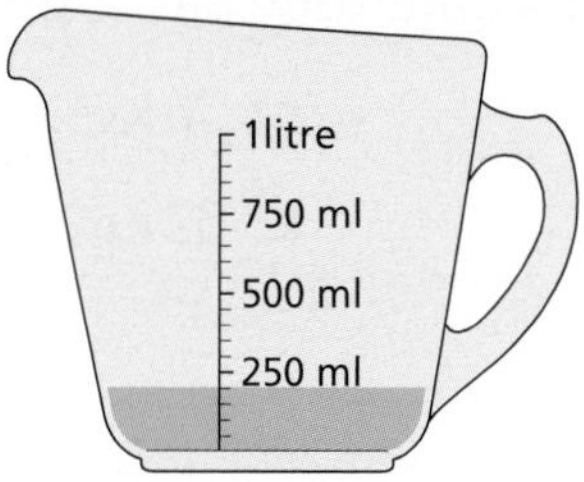

b)

c) 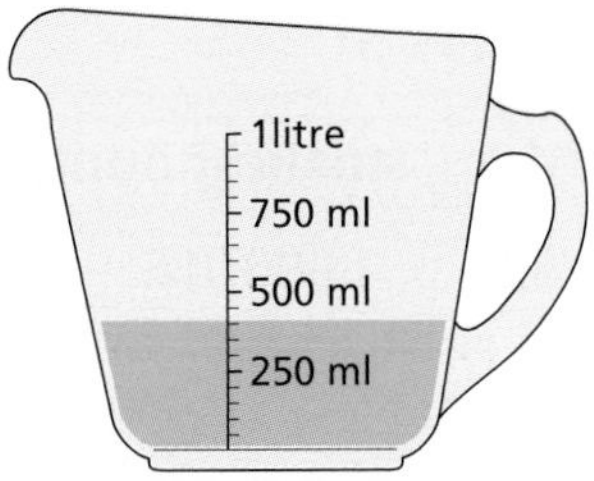

d) 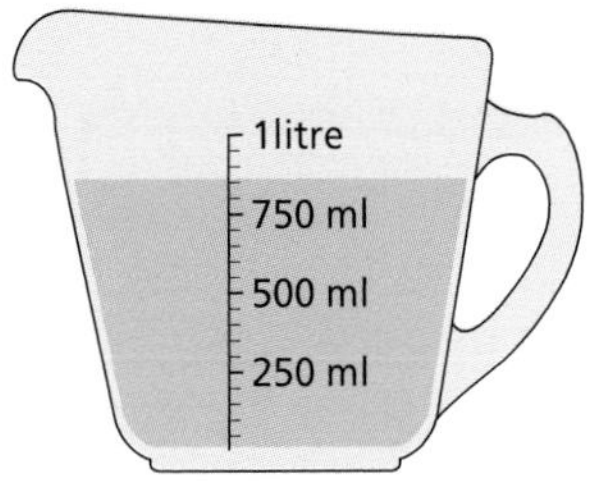

e) 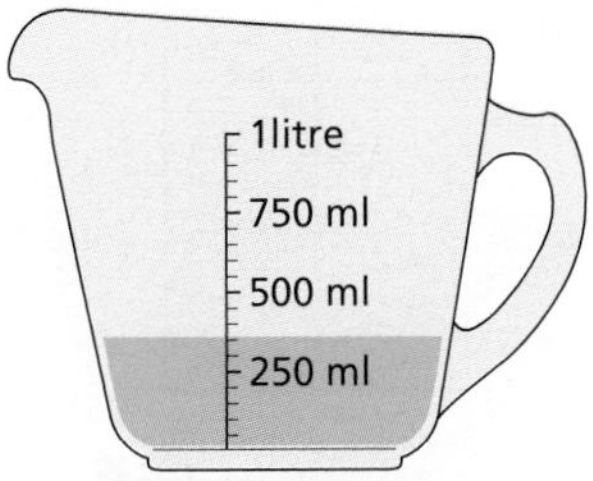

f) 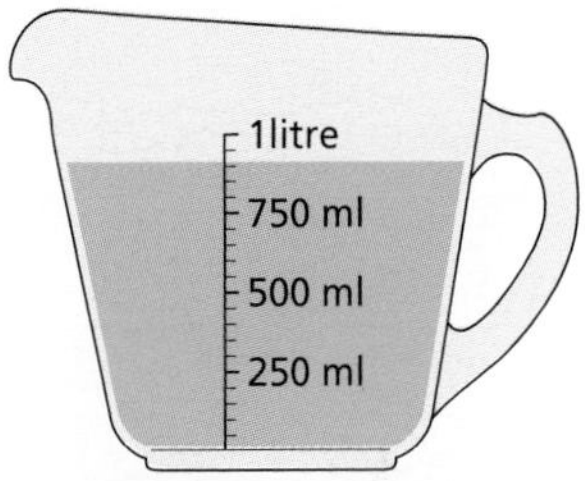

29 Sara wants to make some chocolate mousse for herself and three friends.

Chocolate mousse *(Serves 4 people)*

200 g chocolate
100 ml milk
120 ml water
4 eggs
40 g sugar
1 teaspoon brandy

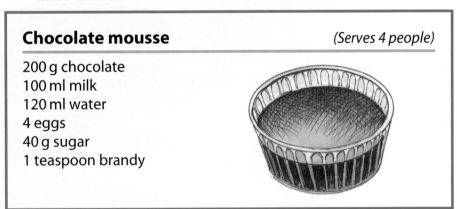

How would she have to change the recipe if she wanted to make mousse for:

a) 8 people? b) 2 people? c) 12 people?

d) only herself?

30 Now try Worksheet 6 *Which measure?* and Worksheet 7 *Which unit?*

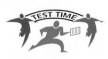

Now try Unit 8 Test.

Review 8

1 Write in order – **smallest** number first.

2016 1.62 1 000 016 106 013 3.62

2 a) Find the **area** and the **perimeter** of this rectangle.

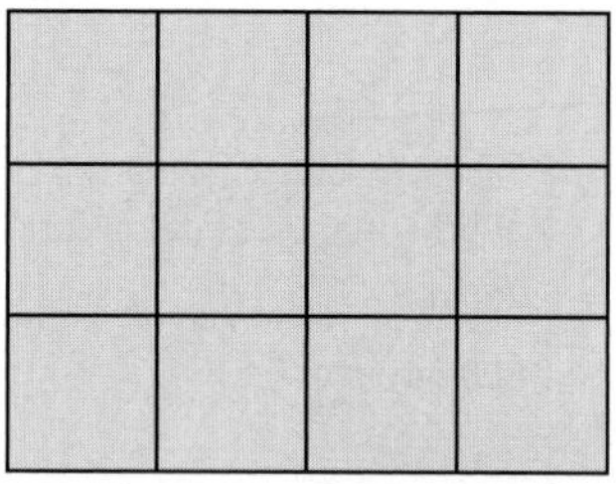

b) A room measures 8 metres wide and 5 metres long. Which of these carpets would fit it with **least** carpet left over?

A 56 square metres **B** 40 square centimetres
C 14 square metres **D** 41 square metres

3 Show if some money is left over, and how much each person gets, if 25 £1 coins are shared between:

a) 2 friends b) 3 friends c) 5 friends d) 4 friends

4 Measure these lines in centimetres and millimetres.

a) ________________________________

b) ________________________

c) ______________________________

5 Look at these thermometers:

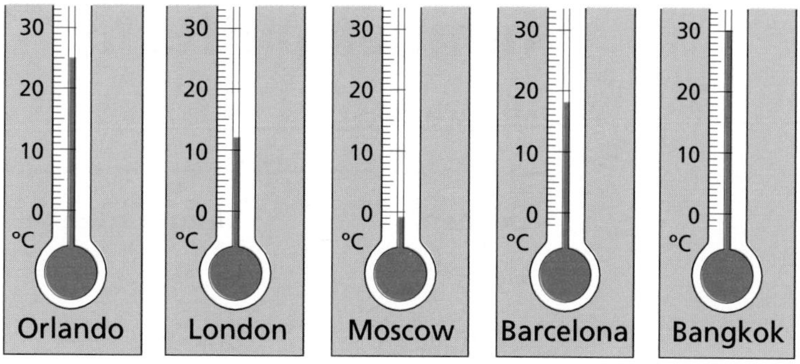

a) What time of year do you think it is?

b) What is the difference between the highest and lowest temperatures given?

6 Leo is reading a book. He reached page **35** on Monday.

On Tuesday he reads **25** more pages, on Wednesday **40** more, on Thursday **50** more and on Friday **35** more to finish.

a) What page did he reach each day?

b) How many pages were there in the whole book?

9 Number

Number patterns

Unit 9 words

borders	**square number**	table
side	share	nearest
multiply	amount	hundred
thousand	approximate	exactly

Remember

Examples are shown in red.

means copy and complete.

You need

- a set of Unit 9 vocabulary Snap cards.

Play a game of Snap to help you learn the words.

Try the **word test** to get some points.

1 You need

- a large piece of centimetre squared paper.

a) Draw a square in the top left-hand corner, a 2 by 2 square and a 3 by 3 square, like this:

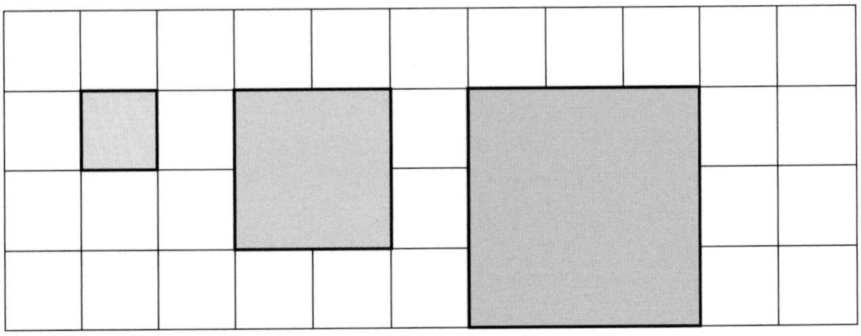

Underneath, write how many small squares are in each large square.

The pattern so far is 1, 4 and 9.
These are known as **square numbers**.
Continue the pattern of squares to find more square numbers.

b) Write what you found in a table like this:

Square	Square number
1	1
2	4
3	9
4	
5	
6	
7	
8	
9	
10	

2 You need

- centimetre squared paper.

If you start with the first square number (1) and add a border (3 squares) down two sides, like this:

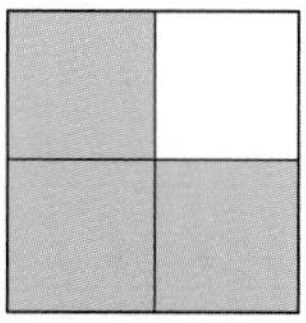

you get the next square number (4).
If you add another border (5 squares) down two sides, like this:

you get the next square number (9).

a) Copy the square border pattern onto squared paper (start near the top right corner).

b) Continue adding L-shaped borders up to the tenth square number.

c) Copy and complete this table.

Border number	Number of squares added	Total
0	1	1
1	3	4
2	5	9
3		
4		
5		
6		
7		
8		
9		

d) What do you notice about each list of numbers you have got?

3 a) Copy and complete this table.

	Total
1 =	1
1 + 3 =	4
1 + 3 + 5 =	9
1 + 3 + 5 + 7 =	
1 + 3 + 5 + 7 + 9 =	
1 + 3 + 5 + 7 + 9 + 11 =	
1 + 3 + 5 + 7 + 9 + 11 + 13 =	
1 + 3 + 5 + 7 + 9 + 11 + 13 + 15 =	
1 + 3 + 5 + 7 + 9 + 11 + 13 + 15 + 17 =	
1 + 3 + 5 + 7 + 9 + 11 + 13 + 15 + 17 + 19 =	

b) What do you notice about the numbers in the Total column?

4 a) Copy and complete this table.

Multiply	Answer
1 × 1	1
2 × 2	
3 × 3	
4 × 4	
5 × 5	
6 × 6	
7 × 7	
8 × 8	
9 × 9	
10 × 10	

Remember

Square numbers are numbers which are made by multiplying a number by itself.

b) What do you notice about the numbers in the Answer column?

5 If you had **ten** £1 coins, you could share them in different ways. You could give them all to one person:

Or you could share them between:
two people

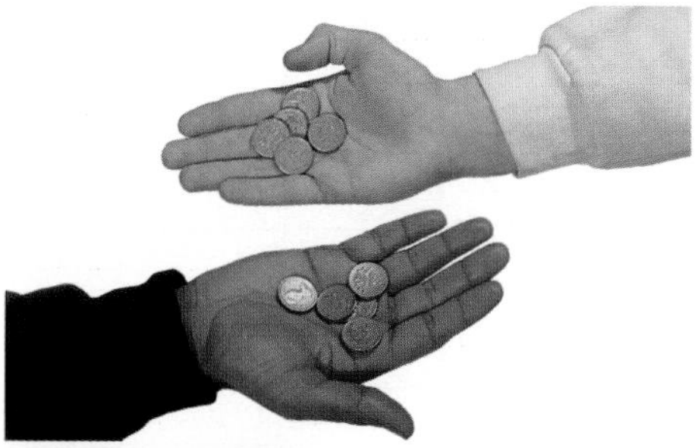

or five people

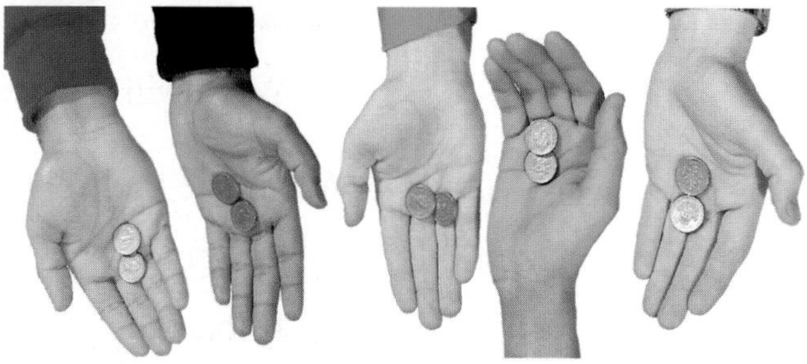

Without changing the coins, could you share them exactly between:

a) six people? b) ten people? c) three people?

d) Write down the numbers of people who could share ten pound coins with none left over.

6 Try Worksheets 1 and 2 *Sharing money (1)* and *(2)*.

7 Look at the pattern these numbers make:

10 ÷ **1** = 10, so **1** divides exactly into 10

10 ÷ **2** = 5, so **2** divides exactly into 10

10 ÷ **5** = 2, so **5** divides exactly into 10

10 ÷ **10** = 1, so **10** divides exactly into 10.

We can say that 10 has four numbers (1, 2, 5 and 10) which divide into it exactly.

a) Will 6 divide exactly into 10?

Work out all of the numbers which will **divide exactly** into:

b) 4 c) 5 d) 6 e) 7 f) 8

8 Now try Worksheets 3 and 4 *Dividing numbers (1)* and *(2)*.

9

£10	£1	10p	1p	
			1p	× 10
		10p		× 10
	£1			× 10
£10				

Tens	Units	Tenths	Hundredths	
0	0	0	1	× 10
0	0	1	0	× 10
0	1	0	0	× 10
1	0	0	0	

a) When we multiply each amount by 10, what happens?

b) What will the next amount be in the tables?

When we multiply money by ten:

c) 1p becomes ☐p d) 10p becomes £☐

e) £1 becomes £☐ f) £10 becomes £☐

10 Try multiplying these amounts of money by 10 in your head.

a) £1 b) £10 c) £0.10 d) 10p

e) 1p f) £1.00 g) £0.01

11 You need

- a calculator.

Multiply the 2p by 10. Multiply each answer by 10.

	£s Ten thousands	£s Thousands	£s Hundreds	£s Tens	£s Units	10ps Tenths	1ps Hundredths	
					0	0	2	× 10
a)								× 10
b)								× 10
c)								× 10
d)								

e) What happens to the 2 each time?

12

£100	£10	£1	10p	1p	
				1p	× 100
		£1			× 100
£100					

Hundreds	Tens	Units	Tenths	Hundredths	
0	0	0	0	1	× 100
0	0	1	0	0	× 100
1	0	0	0	0	

a) When we multiply each amount by 100, what happens?

b) What will the next amount be in each table?

When we multiply money by a hundred:

c) 1p becomes £☐

d) £1 becomes £☐

13 Try multiplying these amounts of money by 100 in your head.

a) £1 b) £10 c) £0.10 d) 10p

e) 1p f) £1.00 g) £0.01

Check your answers with a calculator.

14

£10	£1	10p	1p	
£10				÷ 10
	£1			÷ 10
		10p		÷ 10
			1p	

Tens	Units	Tenths	Hundredths	
1	0	0	0	÷ 10
0	1	0	0	÷ 10
0	0	1	0	÷ 10
0	0	0	1	

a) When we divide each amount by 10, what happens?

When we divide money by 10:

b) £10 becomes £☐

c) £1 becomes ☐p

d) 10p becomes ☐p

15 Now try dividing these amounts by 10 in your head.

a) £1 b) £0.10 c) £10 d) £1.00

e) £10.00 f) 10p

Check your answers with a calculator.

16 You need

- a calculator.

Try putting these numbers into your calculator and pressing [=] each time.

a) 2.40 b) 2.400 c) 2.4000

d) 2.400 000 e) 2.4

f) What do you notice? Why do you think this is?

17 Divide these amounts by 10.

a) £2.40 b) £24 c) £204

d) £20.40 e) £240

Use a calculator to check your answers.

18

£100	£10	£1	10p	1p	
£100					÷ 100
		£1			÷ 100
				1p	

Hundreds	Tens	Units	Tenths	Hundredths	
1	0	0	0	0	÷ 100
0	0	1	0	0	÷ 100
0	0	0	0	1	

a) When we divide each amount by 100, what happens?

When we divide money by a hundred:

b) £100 becomes £☐

c) £10 becomes ☐p

d) £1 becomes ☐p

19 Try dividing these amounts of money by 100 in your head.

a) £100 b) £10 c) £100.00 d) 100p

e) £1 f) £1.00 g) £10.00 h) £24

i) £204 j) £2040 k) £2400 l) £240

Check your answers with a calculator.

Remember

You round up to **pounds (£)** if there is 50p or more, and down if there is less than 50p.

20 Sometimes we **round** answers to the nearest pound (£).
Divide these amounts of money by 100.
Round the answers to the nearest pound.

a) £210 ÷ 100 = £2.10 → £2.00 to the nearest pound (£)

b) £240 c) £204 d) £360

e) £306 f) £86

21 Now try Worksheet 5 *Money rounds*.

Remember

Multiplying and dividing metres and centimetres by 10 is exactly the same as multiplying and dividing pounds and pence.

22 1 millimetre × 10 is 1 centimetre.

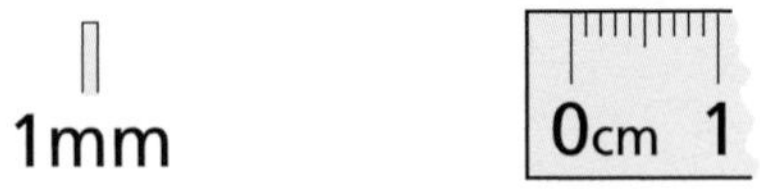

Multiply these millimetres by 10.

a) 5 mm × 10 = 5 cm

b) 3 mm c) 8 mm d) 4 mm e) 6 mm

23 1 centimetre × 10 is 10 centimetres.

Multiply these centimetres by 10.

a) 5 cm × 10 = 50 cm

b) 3 cm c) 8 cm d) 4 cm e) 6 cm

24 10 centimetres × 10 is 100 centimetres or a **metre**.
Multiply these 10s of centimetres by 10 and give your answers in centimetres and in metres.

a) 50 cm × 10 = 500 cm or 5 m

b) 30 cm c) 80 cm d) 40 cm e) 60 cm

25 1 cm divided by 10 is 1 mm.

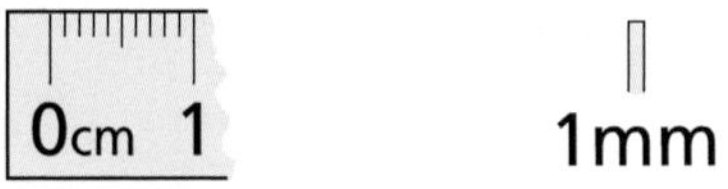

Divide these centimetres by 10.

a) 5 cm ÷ 10 = 5 mm

b) 3 cm c) 8 cm d) 4 cm e) 6 cm

26 10 centimetres divided by 10 is 1 cm.

Divide these 10s of centimetres by 10.

a) 50 cm ÷ 10 = 5 cm

b) 30 cm c) 80 cm d) 40 cm e) 60 cm

27 1 metre or 100 centimetres divided by 10 is 10 cm.
Divide these metres by 10.

a) 5 m = 500 cm 500 cm ÷ 10 = 50 cm

b) 3 m c) 8 m d) 4 m e) 6 m

28 1 metre or 100 centimetres divided by 100 is 1 cm.
Divide these metres by 100.

a) 5 m = 500 cm 500 cm ÷ 100 = 5 cm

b) 3 m c) 8 m d) 4 m e) 6 m

29 Now try Worksheet 6 *Measured problems*.

30 Find the rule for these number patterns.
The rule is:

×10, ×100, ÷10 or **÷100.**

a) 1000 100 10 1 0.1 0.01

b) 2.4 240 24 000 2 400 000 240 000 000

c) 3 600 000 36 000 360 3.6

d) 0.02 0.2 2 20 200 2000

e) 0.59 59 5900 590 000 59 000 000

f) 30 000 3000 300 30 3 0.3 0.03

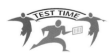

Now try Unit 9 Test.

Review 9

1 In a survey of car sales,  stands for 1000 cars.

How many cars do the following stand for?

a) 

b) 

c) 

d) 

2 What is the **probability** or **chance** each time, of picking a number **ending in zero**?

a) 20 24

b) 10 63 15

c) 60 35 30

d) 20 4 30 98

e) 30 41 80 90

3 How many days are there in:

a) 1 week? b) 7 weeks? c) 9 weeks?

d) $21 \times 3 = \square$

e) $24 \times 6 = \square$

f) $58 \times 7 = \square$

g) $89 \times 9 = \square$

4 Una cleaned her room from 10:45 to 11:10.

a) How long did it take her to clean the room?

How long would it take her if she spent:

b) twice as long? c) half as long?

5 How many **cubic centimetres (cm^3)** is each of these shapes?

a)

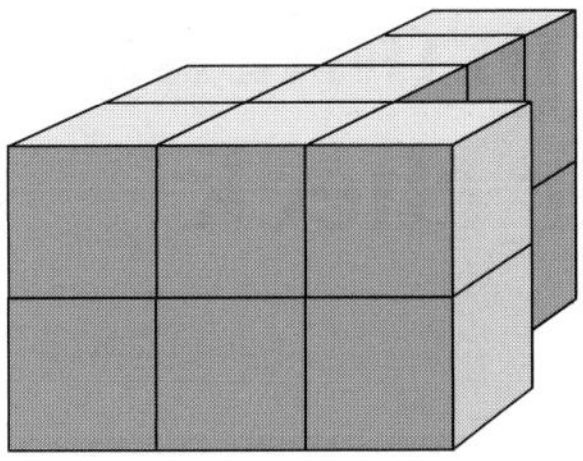

b)

c)

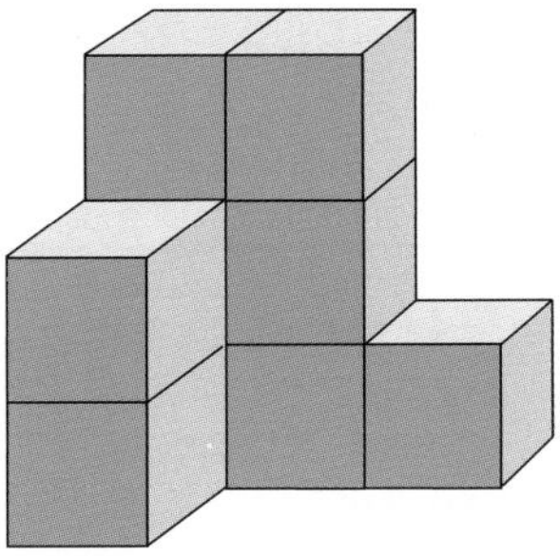

6 10% of a group of **twenty** people were men.
How many were:

a) men?

b) women?

c) What percentage were women?

d) Find 25% and 50% of the group of twenty.

10 Number

Solving problems – estimate, round or check

Unit 10 words

too much	**too little**	**about right**
none	**total cost**	**over**
under	**third**	**bundle**
at least	division	multiplication

Remember

Examples are shown in red.

means copy and complete.

You need

- a set of Unit 10 vocabulary Snap cards.

Play a game of Snap to help you learn the words.

Try the **word test** to get some points.

1 You need

- a calculator.

Three people plan a holiday. The trip costs each person £436. Use a calculator to find out what they pay the travel agent altogether.

2 You may have used your calculator to **add** or **multiply** to find out the answer to Question 1.

Remember

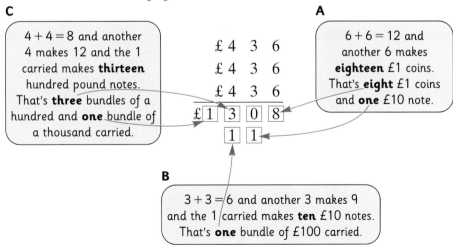

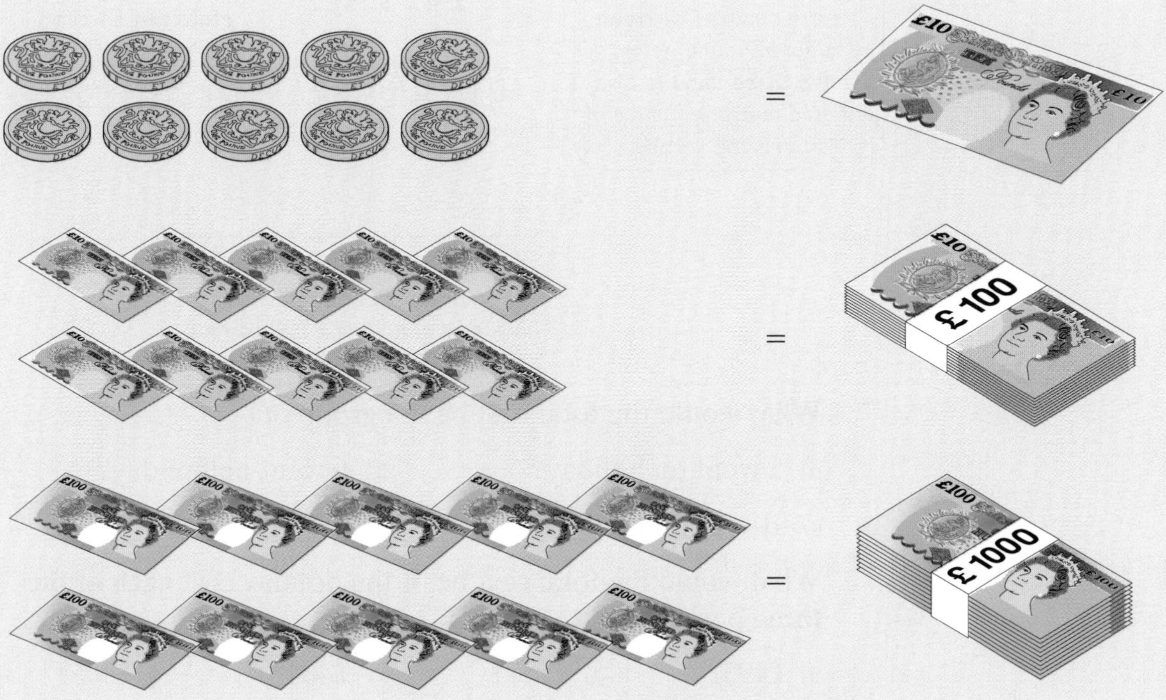

You can work out the answer **on paper**.
You can **add** on paper like this.

	£	4	3	6
	£	4	3	6
	£	4	3	6
£	1	3	0	8
		1	1	

C

4 + 4 = 8 and another 4 makes 12 and the 1 carried makes **thirteen** hundred pound notes. That's **three** bundles of a hundred and **one** bundle of a thousand carried.

A

6 + 6 = 12 and another 6 makes **eighteen** £1 coins. That's **eight** £1 coins and **one** £10 note.

B

3 + 3 = 6 and another 3 makes 9 and the 1 carried makes **ten** £10 notes. That's **one** bundle of £100 carried.

Or you can work it out a much quicker way by **multiplying** on paper like this.

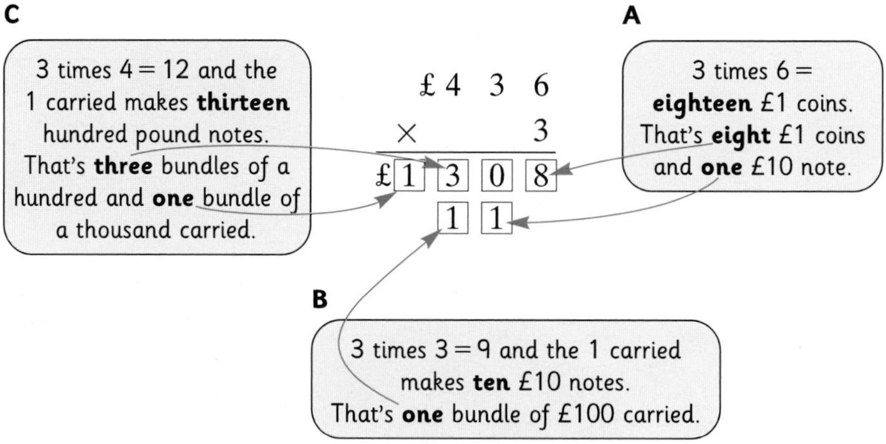

C

3 times 4 = 12 and the 1 carried makes **thirteen** hundred pound notes. That's **three** bundles of a hundred and **one** bundle of a thousand carried.

A

3 times 6 = **eighteen** £1 coins. That's **eight** £1 coins and **one** £10 note.

B

3 times 3 = 9 and the 1 carried makes **ten** £10 notes. That's **one** bundle of £100 carried.

$$\begin{array}{r} £4\ 3\ 6 \\ \times\qquad 3 \\ \hline £1\ 3\ 0\ 8 \\ 1\ 1 \end{array}$$

What would the total cost be if a group of:

a) 5 went on holiday? b) 6 went on holiday?

c) 10 went on holiday?

What would the total cost be, if the holiday cost **each of the three** people:

d) £493? e) £217? f) £404? g) £305?

You can use a calculator to check your answers after you have done them on paper.

3 You need

- a calculator.

Use **multiplication** to check these **addition** answers. Answer **right** or **wrong**.

a) 404 + 404 + 404 + 404 = 1616

b) 147 + 147 + 147 + 147 = 500

c) 289 + 289 + 289 + 289 + 289 = 1445

d) 529 + 529 + 529 + 529 = 2010

e) 155 + 155 + 155 + 155 + 155 + 155 + 155 + 155 + 155 + 155 = 1550

4 Can you find the answers to these using just **multiplication** instead of **addition**?
Answer **yes** or **no**.

a) 404 + 404 + 404 + 213

b) 537 + 537 + 537 + 537 + 537 + 537 + 537 + 537 + 537

c) 260 + 260

d) 235 + 412 + 43 + 2

5 Round each of these amounts to the nearest 10p, nearest pound (£) or nearest ten pounds (£10) to give a quick rough answer.
You can work them out afterwards to see how near your answers were.

a) 45p + 31p + 93p

b) 72p + 89p + 12p

c) 33p + 58p + 11p

d) £2.43 + £4.98 + £3.02

e) £7.50 + £2.09 + £5.86

f) £38 + £64 + £51

g) £23.90 + £35.10 + £10.09

6 To get a rough answer, what number would you round these amounts to – **tens**, **hundreds** or **thousands**?

a) £390

b) £456.23

c) £2500

d) £4872.02

e) In which of the above amounts did the pence matter least?

7 Gill has a meal out once a week.
Work out the amounts roughly in your head to see if Gill's bills are likely to be correct.

Answer **too much**, **too little** or **about right**.

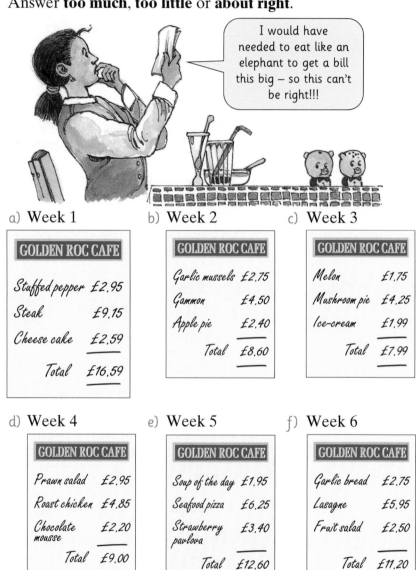

I would have needed to eat like an elephant to get a bill this big – so this can't be right!!!

a) Week 1

GOLDEN ROC CAFE	
Stuffed pepper	£2.95
Steak	£9.15
Cheese cake	£2.59
Total	£16.59

b) Week 2

GOLDEN ROC CAFE	
Garlic mussels	£2.75
Gammon	£4.50
Apple pie	£2.40
Total	£8.60

c) Week 3

GOLDEN ROC CAFE	
Melon	£1.75
Mushroom pie	£4.25
Ice-cream	£1.99
Total	£7.99

d) Week 4

GOLDEN ROC CAFE	
Prawn salad	£2.95
Roast chicken	£4.85
Chocolate mousse	£2.20
Total	£9.00

e) Week 5

GOLDEN ROC CAFE	
Soup of the day	£1.95
Seafood pizza	£6.25
Strawberry pavlova	£3.40
Total	£12.60

f) Week 6

GOLDEN ROC CAFE	
Garlic bread	£2.75
Lasagne	£5.95
Fruit salad	£2.50
Total	£11.20

Without working out the answers exactly, estimate which weeks Gill spent:

g) over £10 on her meal out

h) under £10 on her meal out

i) about £10 on her meal out

8 By working out the amounts roughly in your head, see if Gill's change is likely to be correct. She gave £20 each time. Answer **too much**, **too little** or **about right**.

a) Bill total £9.80

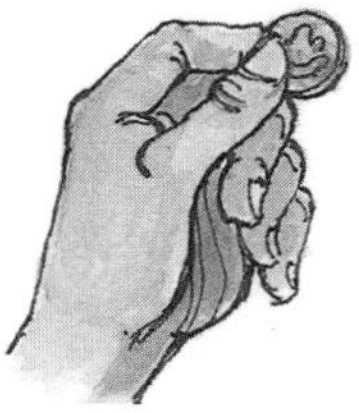

I gave them £20, so this can't be right!

This amount of change is too little.

b) Bill total £11.60

c) Bill total £4.90

d) Bill total £15.30

e) Bill total £14.85

Remember

1 kg = 1000 g

9 Kelly does a paper round. She goes to six rows of houses and delivers papers to four houses in each of the rows. Sunday papers are the heaviest. They weigh about 750 g each.

a) The Sunday papers for each row weigh ☐ g or ☐ kg.

b) On Sundays, Kelly's bag weighs ☐ g or ☐ kg when she starts her paper round.

It weighs:

c) ☐ g or ☐ kg after she finishes the first row.

d) ☐ g or ☐ kg after she finishes the second row.

e) ☐ g or ☐ kg after she finishes the third row.

10 You need

- a calculator.

> **Remember**
>
> You can use multiplication to check division.
> Example: $6 \div 2 = 3$ or $3 \times 2 = 6$

> **Remember**
>
> Add on any remainders.

Use **multiplication** to check these **division** answers.
Answer **right** or **wrong**.

a) $200 \div 2 = 100$ b) $175 \div 5 = 35$ c) $1200 \div 10 = 12$

d) $127 \div 4 = 31$ e) $179 \div 5 = 35$ r 4 f) $1207 \div 10 = 120$ r 7

g) $1322 \div 7 = 145$ h) $300 \div 5 = 65$ r 5 i) $263 \div 10 = 26$ r 3

11 a) $6 \div 2 = \square$ b) $2 \times \square = 6$

c) $21 \div 3 = \square$ d) $3 \times \square = 21$

e) $12 \div 4 = \square$ f) $4 \times \square = 12$

g) $28 \div 4 = \square$ h) $4 \times \square = 28$

i) $56 \div 7 = \square$ j) $7 \times \square = 56$

k) $81 \div 9 = \square$ l) $9 \times \square = 81$

m) $72 \div 8 = \square$ n) $8 \times \square = 72$

o) $32 \div 8 = \square$ p) $8 \times \square = 32$

q) $30 \div 6 = \square$ r) $6 \times \square = 30$

s) $300 \div 6 = \square$ t) $6 \times \square = 300$

12 a) Can you tell at a glance if a number can be divided **by 10**? Do some examples to see if you are right.

b) Can you tell at a glance if a number can be divided **by 5**? Do some examples to see if you are right.

13 You can use

- a calculator. 

Sal and Pete run a garden centre. They have **240** seeds to plant.

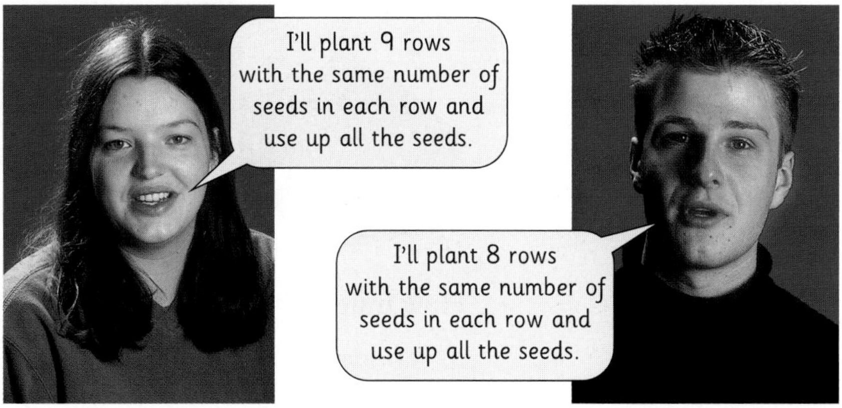

I'll plant 9 rows with the same number of seeds in each row and use up all the seeds.
I'll plant 8 rows with the same number of seeds in each row and use up all the seeds.

a) Who is right?

b) Why is the other person wrong?

Complete the table to show some of the different ways they could plant the 240 seeds in rows so that none will be left over.

Rows	Number of seeds in a row
c) 2 rows	120 seeds
d) ☐ rows	80 seeds
e) 6 rows	☐ seeds
f) ☐ rows	60 seeds
g) ☐ rows	24 seeds
h) 5 rows	☐ seeds

Could you plant:

i) 2300 seeds in 10 rows?

j) 2335 seeds in 10 rows?

k) 785 seeds in 5 rows?

l) 785 seeds in 10 rows?

14 Now try Worksheets 1 and 2 *Which method? (1)* and *(2)*.

15 You can use

- a calculator.

Lin plans a Christmas party.
She makes bows for presents.

It takes 20 cm of ribbon to make this bow.

How much ribbon would it take to make:

a) 5 bows? b) 7 bows? c) 10 bows?

d) 4 bows? e) 12 bows?

Which of these lengths of ribbon could Lin use to make bows and have no ribbon left over?

f) 60 cm g) 1 m h) 310 cm

i) $1\frac{1}{4}$m j) $1\frac{1}{2}$m

Without working out the answer, can you think of a quick way to say if the following answers are right or wrong?
Use your calculator to check.

k) Gill makes bows which measure:
30 cm + 30 cm + 30 cm + 30 cm + 30 cm + 30 cm.
Altogether she uses 180 cm.

l) Gill uses about $\frac{1}{4}$m to make bows which measure:
51 cm, 25 cm, 102 cm and 72 cm.

16 Lin also prepares drinks for the party.
She makes diluted orange juice for the children.
She dilutes the orange by mixing it with four times as much water as orange.
She has a one litre bottle of orange drink to dilute.

a) When she dilutes it, how much orange juice will she make?

How much will she make if she has:

b) $\frac{1}{4}$l to dilute? c) $\frac{1}{2}$l to dilute? d) 200 ml to dilute?

Lin drinks water.

I drink at least **eight glasses** of water **a day** to keep healthy.

If a medium glass holds 250 ml of water –

e) how many glasses will Lin drink in a day if she drinks 1 litre?

f) Will that be enough for her to keep healthy?

If she drinks 8 glasses a day, how much water will she drink in:

g) a day? h) a week? i) a month? j) a year?

17 You need

- a measuring cylinder from the science lab
- a water tap
- a calculator.

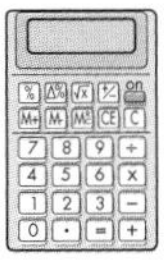

a) Turn a tap so that it is dripping as slowly as possible.

b) Measure how much it drips in **5 minutes**.

c) Work out how much it would drip in one hour, then one day, one week, one month and one year.

d) Find out how much water is lost through dripping taps and pipes in your area and different ways that lost water could have been used.
Try to make your own estimate of how much water may be lost before you find out.
Set out all your work clearly so that you can show your results to the rest of the group.

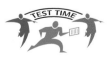

Now try Unit 10 Test.

Review 10

1 Round these amounts to the nearest pound (£), add and write the answers.

a) £28.96 + £7.36

b) £52.25 + £13.72

c) £450.18 + £99.86

Check the **exact** answers using a calculator.

How near was each answer you did in your head?

Round these amounts to the nearest litre, add and write the answers.

d) 1 litre 20 ml + 2 litres 795 ml

e) 10 litres 950 ml + 10 litres 300 ml

2 Measure the radius below and find the diameter of the circle.

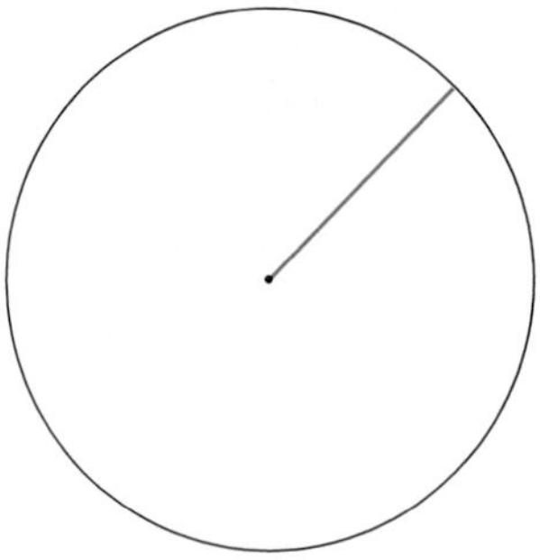

3 Find 50%, 25%, 10% and 5% of:

a) £800

b) £1000

c) 1 kg

d) £900

e) 120 litres

4 What part is shaded?

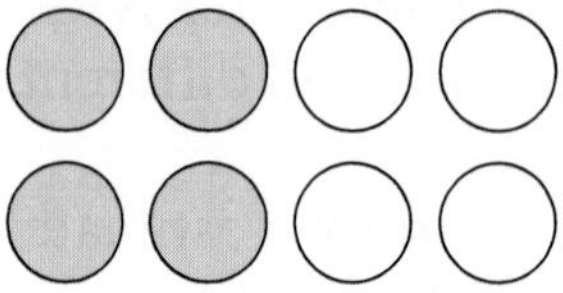

Write your answer as a fraction, a percentage and a decimal.

5 a) Rosie is 1.65 m tall. Her sister is 153 cm tall.
How much taller is Rosie than her sister?

b) You have a rope 1 m long. You cut off 4 pieces of 10 cm.
How long is the rope now?

6 These people save monthly for a holiday.
Gina saves £43. Saeed saves £55. Tina saves £78.

a) How much will they save altogether in one month?

b) How much more than Gina does Tina save per month?

c) How much less than Saeed does Gina save per month?

d) How much will **each** save in 5 months?

e) If you want to save £1450 in ten months, how much would you need to save per month?

11 Revision

Unit 11 words

net pay	**basic pay**	longest
bottom	week	hours
months	years	value
estimate	graph	pictogram

Remember

Examples are shown in red.

means copy and complete.

You need

- a set of Unit 11 vocabulary Snap cards.

Play a game of Snap to help you learn the words.

Try the **word test** to get some points.

1 Carol Hale and Dan Jackson got jobs in two different supermarkets.

MORRISONS
I work for Stars
in the town of Bede.

Dairy
I work for Trustco's
in the town of Bede.

The two supermarkets open at the following times.

Stars Supermarkets

OPENING TIMES

Mon	9.00 a.m. to 8.00 p.m.
Tues	9.00 a.m. to 8.00 p.m.
Wed	9.00 a.m. to 8.00 p.m.
Thurs	9.00 a.m. to midnight
Fri	24 hours
Sat	7.00 a.m. to 9.00 p.m.
Sun	9.00 a.m. to 4.00 p.m.

Trustco's Supermarkets

OPENING TIMES

Mon	8.00 a.m. to 8.00 p.m.
Tues	8.00 a.m. to 8.00 p.m.
Wed	8.00 a.m. to midnight
Thurs	24 hours
Fri	8.00 a.m. to 8.00 p.m.
Sat	8.00 a.m. to 9.00 p.m.
Sun	9.00 a.m. to 3.00 p.m.

Answer **yes** or **no** to the following questions.
Could you go shopping at **Stars** supermarket at:

a) 8.30 p.m. on Monday?
b) 8.30 p.m. on Saturday?
c) 4.30 a.m. on Wednesday?
d) 4.30 a.m. on Friday?
e) 8.50 a.m. on Saturday?
f) 15.45 on Sunday?

Could you go shopping at **Trustco's** supermarket at:

g) 8.30 a.m. on Monday?
h) 9.30 p.m. on Saturday?
i) 4.30 a.m. on Wednesday?
j) 4.30 a.m. on Thursday?
k) 2.55 p.m. on Sunday?
l) 22:00 on Wednesday?

2 How many hours does **Stars** supermarket open:

a) each day?
b) each week?

How many hours does **Trustco's** supermarket open:

c) each day?
d) each week?

e) ____________________ supermarket opens longest each week.

f) It opens ☐ hours longer.

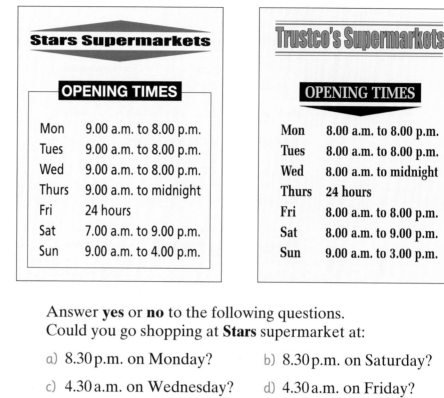

3 Carol and Dan get paid every week.
Here are their pay slips.

Stars Supermarkets		Pay advice		Week ending 31-3-2001	
Payee no. 240	Tax year 2000/2001	Employees name CAROL HALE		Tax code 438L	N.I. number DH80423C
Basic pay	£180.00	Code	Value	Tax	£17.55
Total deductions	£27.95	101	£180.00	N.I.	£10.40
NET PAY					

Trustco's Supermarkets		Pay advice		Week ending 31-3-2001	
Payee no. 154	Tax year 2000/2001	Employees name DAN JACKSON		Tax code 347L	N.I. number NW90480B
Basic pay	£245.00	Code	Value	Tax	£35.71
Total deductions	£52.61	123	£245	N.I.	£16.90
NET PAY					

Pay slips give you a lot of information.
They tell you:

- what you are paid
- what is taken off, e.g. in tax
- the money you take home – **net pay**.

a) In which month were these pay slips given?

b) Which part of the pay slip do you think most people look at first?

Tax years begin in April.

c) What tax year will be written on the next pay slip?

d) Carol earns £______ basic pay per week.

e) She pays £______ tax.

f) She pays £______ National Insurance.

g) Her net pay is £______.

h) Dan earns £☐ basic pay per week.

i) He pays £☐ tax.

j) He pays £☐ National Insurance.

k) His net pay is £☐.

l) How much more than Carol does Dan get paid each week?

m) Why do you think this might be?

About how much do Carol and Dan get paid net:

n) in a month? o) in a year?

4 This is the fruit and vegetable section at Trustco's.

They have some special offers.

a) How much would you really pay for one of these melons?

b) Can you think of other ways they could have made the offer? Would they have been as good as this way?

c) How much was saved on the reduced strawberries (above)?

On the shelf below there were some strawberries that were **not reduced**.

d) Which strawberries were the best buy? Explain how you worked out your answer.

5 Now try Worksheet 1 *Vegetable workout.*

6 We buy **larger** quantities if we can because they are sometimes cheaper, but not always!

a) 500 g × 3 = ☐ g

b) Three (500 g) packets of Bran Flakes cost £☐.☐☐.

c) 750 g × 2 = ☐ g

d) Two (750 g) packets of Bran Flakes cost £☐.☐☐.

e) Is it better value to buy the smaller or larger packet of Bran Flakes?

7 Which of these is the better value – the pack or the single items?

a)

b)

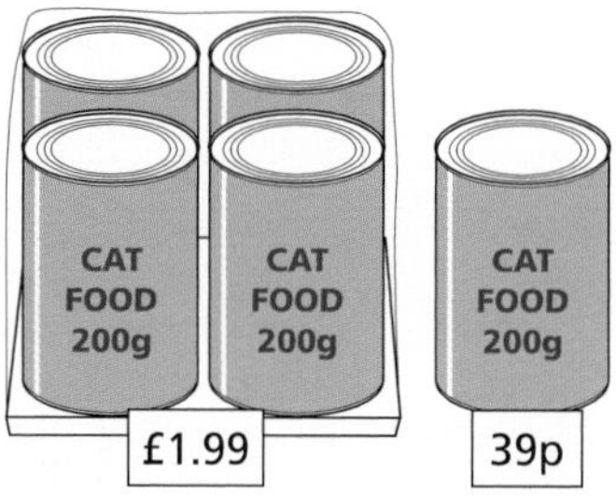

c)

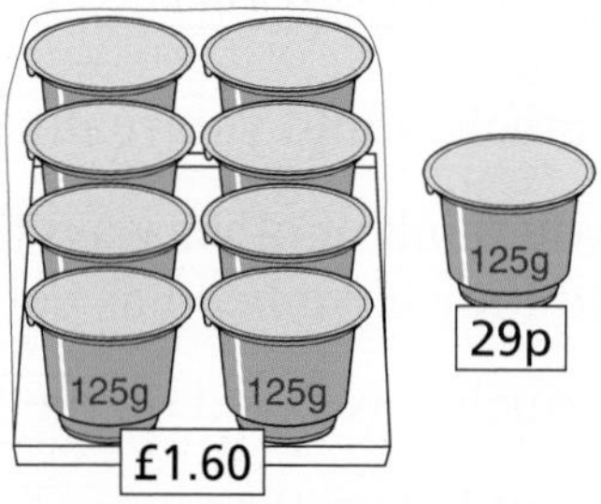

8 Shops often sell things marked with prices such as:

99p £1.99 £2.49 £4.99 £6.49 £9.99

a) Round these prices to the nearest fifty pence (50p) or pound (£).

b) Why don't shops round prices up?

c) Why do you never see prices of £1.01 or £10.01?

9 One supermarket picked out some items. They called them a typical 'shopping basket'. They showed the difference in price between their store and the other supermarket like this.

a) **Without** working out the answers for the total, make an estimate to decide which supermarket has the best prices overall.

Item	Trustco's price	Stars price
1 kg onions	£0.39	£0.38
2 kg potatoes	£4.00	£3.50
1 litre skimmed milk	£0.49	£0.47
6 large eggs (free range)	£1.46	£1.10
1 farmhouse loaf (800 g)	£0.75	£0.74
250 g butter	£0.79	£0.75
1 kg frozen peas	£2.29	£2.27
2 fresh chicken breasts	£2.88	£2.56
1 kg cornflakes	£1.77	£1.76
1 packet tea (160 bags)	£2.49	£2.48
Total		

You may use a calculator.

The total shopping bill for the basket of items:

b) Stars is £______.

c) Trustco's is £______.

d) The difference in price for the total shopping bill is

£______.

10 a) Do you think the supermarket with the cheapest prices overall really is the best value for money?

Talk to your partner or teacher about this.

b) How could you choose the best supermarket for you? (Think of the things that you eat or use regularly.)

11 Dan goes to the warehouse to get stock for Trustco's.
He puts 1 kg bags of sugar on a trolley.
He puts the bottom layer on like this.

a) He can fit ☐ packets of sugar on the bottom layer altogether.

He can fit 10 layers on a trolley.

b) He can fit ☐ packets of sugar on the trolley.

c) The sugar on the trolley weighs ☐ kg when the trolley is fully loaded.

Dan takes the trolley down in a lift.

d) If the lift had a sign which said:

Total weight in lift
must **NOT** be
greater than
500 kg.

should Dan take the full trolley down in the lift?

12 Carol is in charge of Stars bakery.

She plans how many loaves the bakery will make each day.
This pictogram shows the number of loaves sold at the full price of **80p**.

Key:  = 200 loaves.

Day	Number of loaves sold at full price
Monday	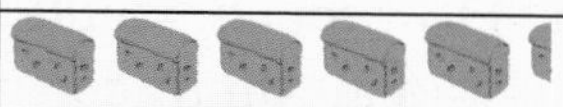
Tuesday	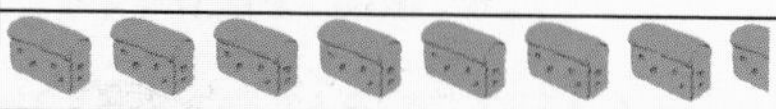
Wednesday	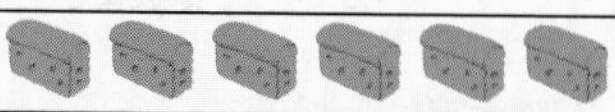
Thursday	
Friday	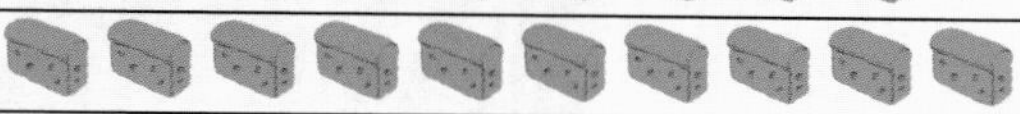
Saturday	
Sunday	

How many loaves would need to be drawn on the table to show:

a) 2200 loaves were sold on Saturday?

b) 800 loaves were sold on Sunday?

On which day were:

c) most loaves sold? d) least loaves sold?

e) How many more loaves were sold on Friday than Monday?

f) Why do you think there were more loaves sold on some days than others?

You may use a calculator. 

g) How many loaves were sold in the whole week?

13 Carol ordered 1400 loaves to be made on Monday.
Loaves not sold by 5.00 p.m. were reduced by 50%. Look back at the table on page 121.

a) How many loaves were reduced?

b) How much did the reduced loaves each cost?

c) If all the reduced loaves were sold on Monday, how much money would the store take for them?

d) How much would they have taken if the loaves had been sold at full price?

14 Sometimes Dan works at the till.

Some friends come to Trustco's.
Without working out the totals, estimate if they will be able to pay for their shopping or not.

Answer **yes** or **no**.

a) Ben has £6.00.

b) Tracey has £10.00.

c) Joe has £15.00.

d) Gale has £7.50.

e) Work out the total for each basket.
How much does each person still **need** to pay or **have left** after paying their bill?

15 Trustco's and Stars have worked hard to get more people in Bede to shop in their stores during the ten years from 1992 to 2002.
Here is information about those ten years shown in two ways.

1980 – Stars open in Bede.
1992 – Trustco's open in Bede.
1993 – Food poisoning from chickens sold in Stars – store closes for three months – renovation carried out.
1994 – New management in Stars.
1997 – Trustco's opens clothing department for children.
2000 – Trustco's introduce their own cheaper brand of foods.
2001 – Sainsbury's supermarket opens in Bede.

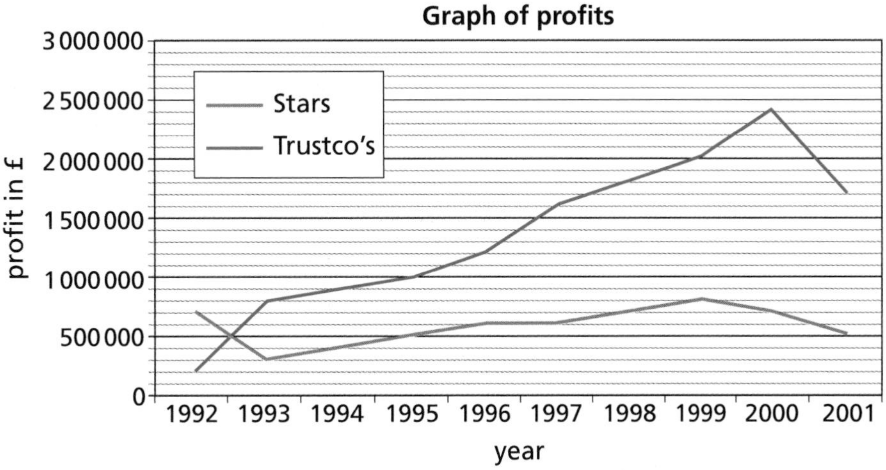

In 1992, how much profit did:

a) Trustco's make?

b) Stars make?

In 2000, how much profit did:

c) Trustco's make?   d) Stars make?

e) Name two things which might have brought about this change.

You need

- a calculator.

From 1992 to 2001, how much money did:

f) Trustco's make?   g) Stars make?

In which year did Trustco's:

h) first earn at least a million pounds profit?

i) profits begin to go down? Why do you think this happened?

In which year did Stars:

j) first earn at least half a million pounds profit?

k) profits go down most? Why do you think this happened?

In 2001, the profits of both stores are going down.
How likely is it that in the future:

l) Trustco's profits will start to rise again?

m) Stars' profits will start to rise again?

Say why you think so.

There is no test in this unit.

12 Revision

Unit 12 words

South East	**North West**	**monthly**
million	temperature	likely
percentage	digit	radius
diameter	area	cube

Remember

Examples are shown in red.

means copy and complete.

You need

- a set of Unit 12 vocabulary Snap cards.

Play a game of Snap to help you learn the words.

Try the **word test** to get some points.

Number

1 What are the temperatures shown below?

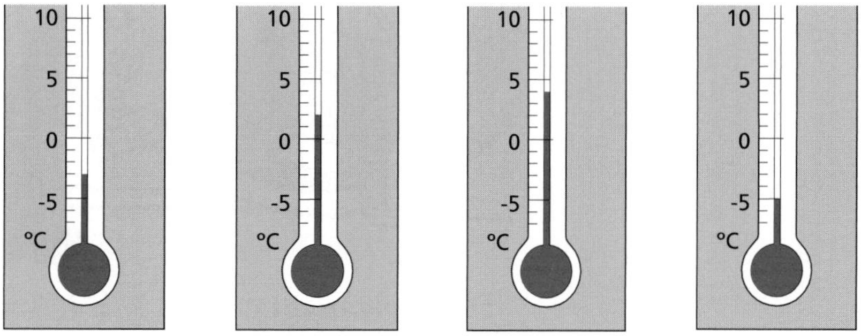

a) ☐ °C b) ☐ °C c) ☐ °C d) ☐ °C

e) What is the temperature rise from a) to b)?

f) What is the temperature fall from c) to d)?

2 Write these temperatures in order, **coldest first**.

30 °C −4 °C 0 °C 17 °C 5 °C −20 °C

3 Tom gets £2000 paid into his bank in June, as his monthly salary.

a) At the end of May he had £250 left in his account. How much does he have now?

b) He has bills for £400 which are taken out. How much has he got left?

4 Now try Worksheet 1 *Sea level.*

5 Which answer is roughly right?

a) 25 356 ÷ 4 is about: 600 6000 60 000 600 000

b) 472 × 9 is about: 500 5000 50 000 500 000

c) 5 × 21 000 is about: 1 thousand 100 thousand 1 million 10 million

d) 104 × 103 is about: 1 thousand 10 thousand 100 thousand 1 million

6 A car factory is putting number plates on cars.

They only use the digits 1, 2, 3, 4 and 5.
Each digit can only be used once on each plate.

a) Make six different **4-digit** number plates.

b) Write these numbers in words.

c) Put them in order, **smallest first**.

7 You need

- a calculator.

a)

Sum	Answer
1 × 1	1
11 × 11	121
111 × 111	
1111 × 1111	

b) What do you notice?

c) Complete the next 3 lines of the table **without** using your calculator.

d) What do you think is the answer to 11 111 111 × 11 111 111?

8 You need

- a calculator.

Use a calculator to check if these sums are correct. Work back from the answer.

a) 65 × 32 = 2080

b) 777 ÷ 37 = 12

c) 55 × 28 = 1504

d) 780 ÷ 26 = 30

e) 44 × 19 = 830

f) 1950 ÷ 30 = 65

9 We could write £1 000 000 as **£1 million** and say **one million pounds**.

We could write £10 000 000 as **£10 million** and say **ten million pounds**.

We could write £100 000 000 as **£100 million** and say **one hundred million pounds**.

In the year 2000, some of the richest people in the world had the following money:

	Country	Estimated wealth (£)
Richard Branson	England	£1740 million
The Moores family	England	£1900 million
Lord Cavendish	England	£2200 million
Lord Sainsbury	England	£3270 million
The Li Ka-shing family	Hong Kong	£8500 million
Michael Dell	USA	£11 000 million
Steven Ballmer	USA	£13 000 million
Paul Allen	USA	£20 000 million
Bill Gates	USA	£65 000 million

Can you say any of the above amounts?
Bill Gates, the owner of Microsoft computer software company had sixty-five billion pounds or sixty-five thousand million pounds!!!!!!!
If he gave away a million pounds a day...

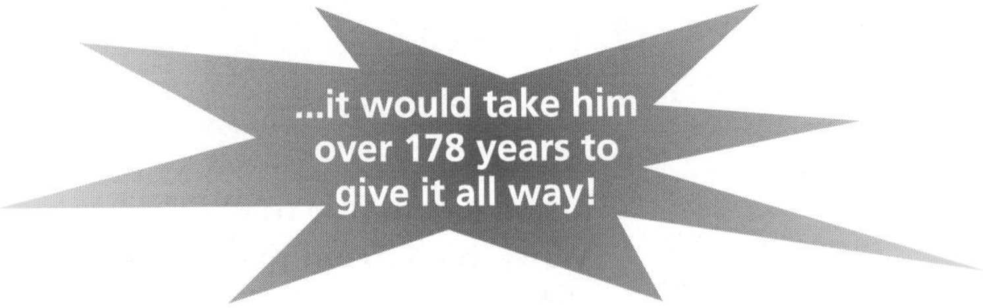
...it would take him over 178 years to give it all way!

You may need a calculator.

If he gave away a million pounds a day, how many millions would he give away:

a) in a week?

b) in a month (4 weeks)?

c) in a year (52 weeks)?

d) in ten years?

e) in a hundred years?

f) Can you work out how many more millions he had than Richard Branson?

Shape and space

10 People can have garden makeovers done by television teams.

Before they begin, they make a plan of the new garden like this.

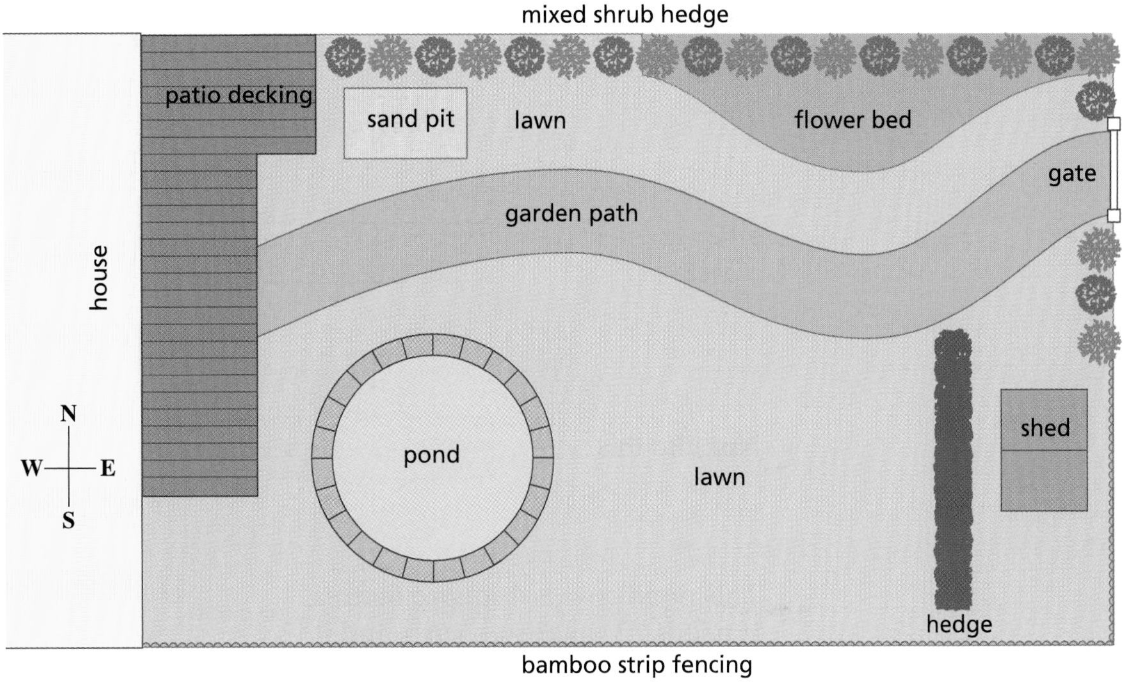

a) What is North of the pond?

b) What is West of the sand pit?

c) What is East of the sand pit?

d) What is North West of the shed?

e) What is North East of the hedge?

11 Now try Worksheet 2 *Plan a garden*.

12 Mick builds garden ponds.

He puts borders of paving slabs around the ponds.
He needs to work out how many he needs for different ponds.
Borders must completely surround the pond like this.

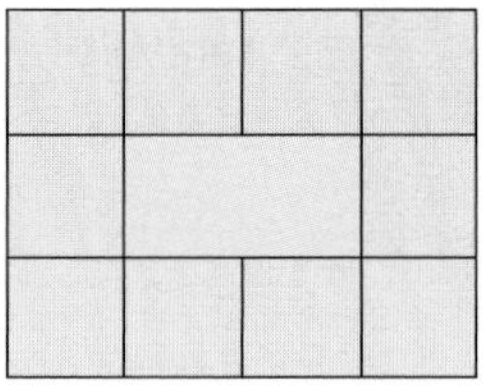

Not like this.

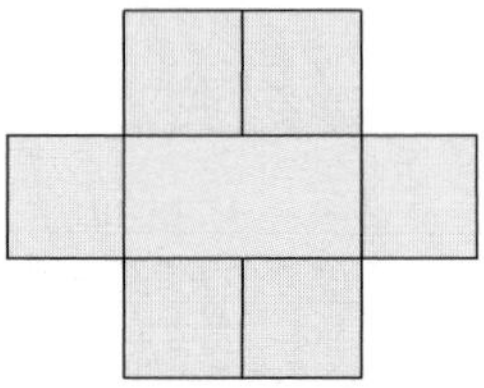

This pond covers 4 square metres.
It needs 12 squares to surround it.

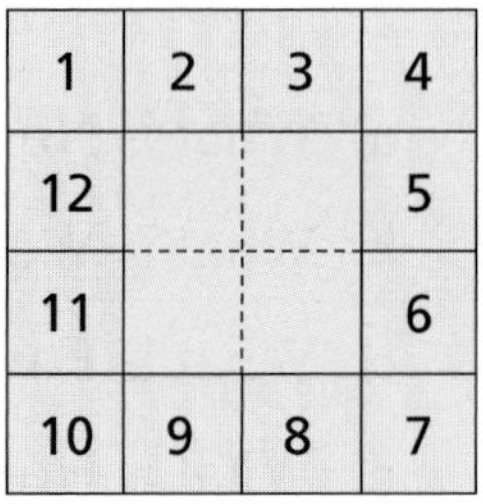

You need

- centimetre squared paper.

Draw different sized ponds on your paper.
Draw borders to work out the number of slabs needed to surround each pond.
Look for a pattern.

13 Draw a pond 3 cm by 4 cm.

a) Write down how many squares there are in your pond.

Do the same for these ponds:

b) 2 cm by 5 cm c) 4 cm by 4 cm d) 4 cm by 3 cm

e) 2 cm by 4 cm f) 3 cm by 5 cm g) 3 cm by 3 cm

h) Do you notice any link between the answers and your times tables?

14 Divide the pond below into two rectangles.

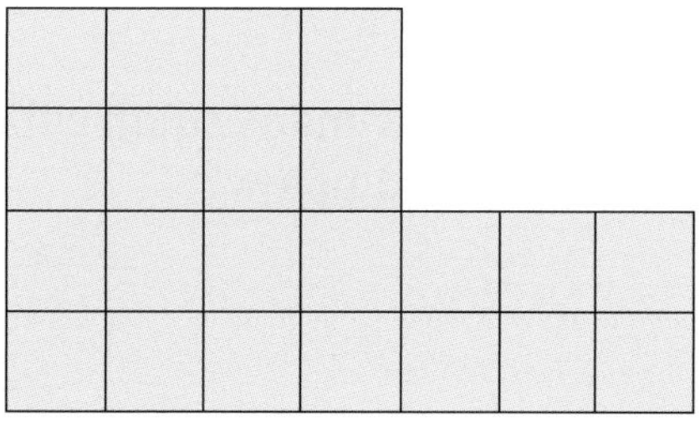

a) Find the area of each rectangle.

b) Find the total area.

c) Draw similar shapes and find their areas.

15 These pictures are all different views of the same dice.

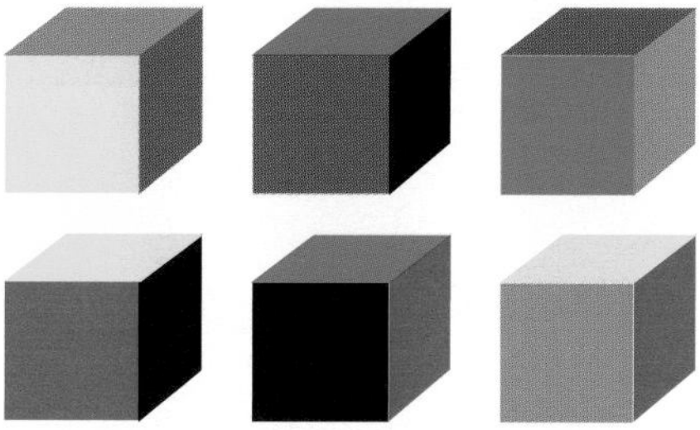

Which colours are opposite each other?

16 Six cubes have been used to make the shape below.

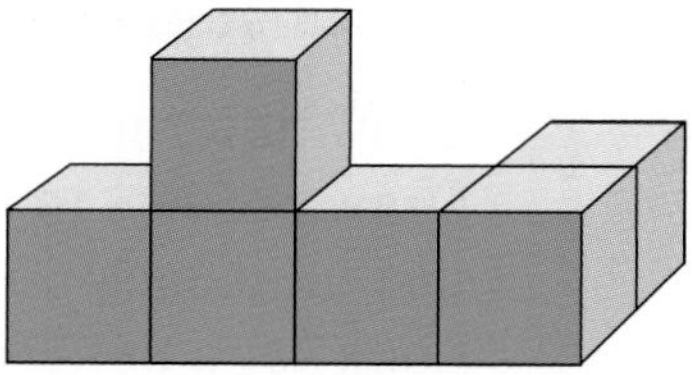

Which of these shapes is the same shape turned round?

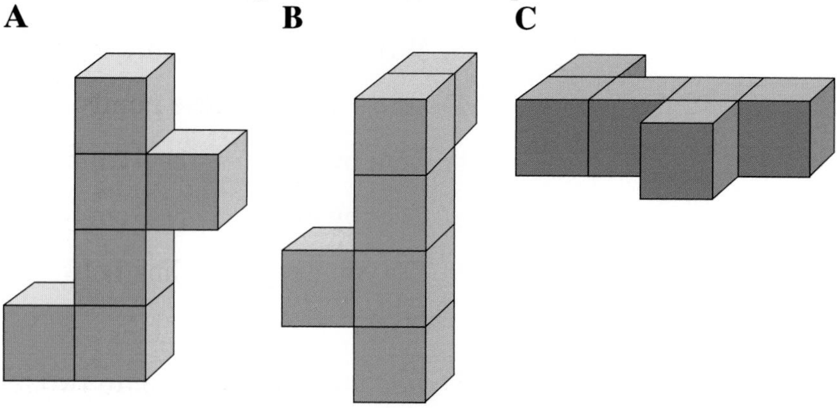

17 How many small cubes are needed to complete the bigger cube below?

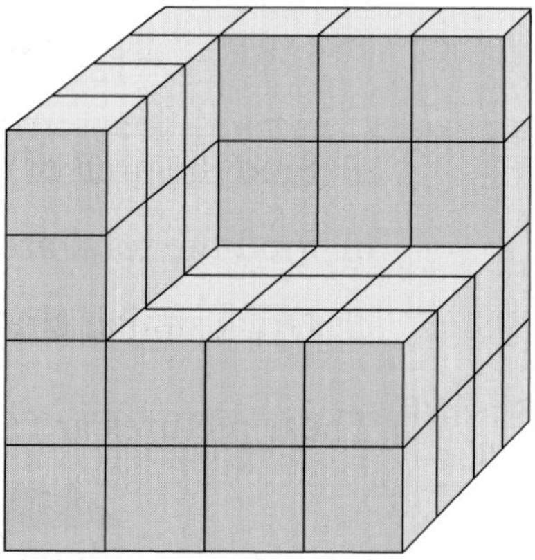

Measures

18 Joe wants to buy a car.
He works out the **monthly** cost of running it.

Item	Monthly cost
Loss of value	£100
Petrol	£100
Insurance	£35
Road tax	£15
Servicing	£30
Repairs	£20

a) How much would it cost him each month to run a car?

Joe's train fares cost him £100 per month.

b) How much more would he have to pay to run a car than travel by train?

Joe's flat mate Ella wants to share **equally** the costs of the car.

c) Ella would pay £______ per month.

d) If Ella shared the costs, Joe would now only pay £______ per month.

19 Now try Worksheet 3 *Starting a business.*

20 When Ali is born he is this long:

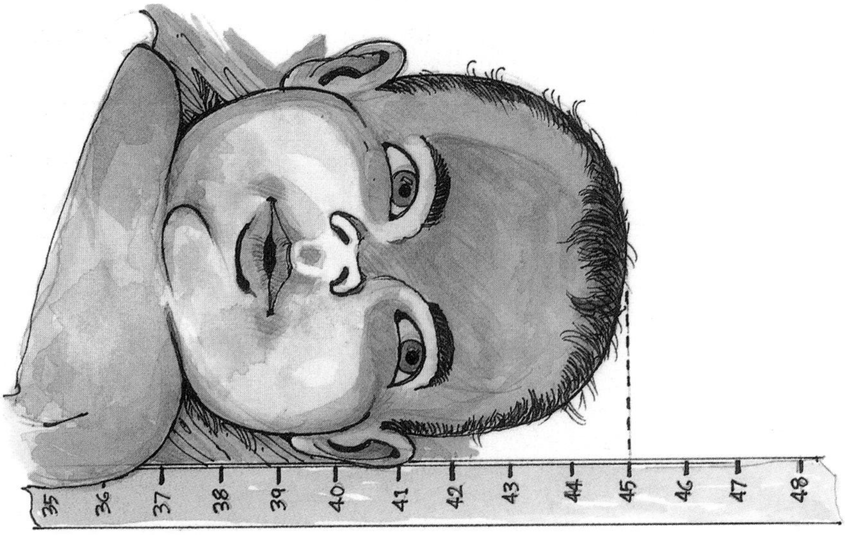

a) How tall is he?

b) His sister is much older than him. She is 1.45 m tall. How tall is she in centimetres?

c) Ali's father is 1 m 80 cm tall. How tall is this in metres as a decimal?

21 Now try Worksheet 4 *Measure problems*.

Handling data

Remember

4% means 4 out of every 100.

22 A 1998 survey looked at smoking rates in different countries. This is a table of the results:

Country	Male (%)	Female (%)
Vietnam	73	4
China	63	4
United Kingdom	29	28
Canada	27	23
USA	26	21
Sweden	17	22
Hong Kong	27	3
Singapore	27	3

Use Worksheet 5 *Smoking facts* to help you.

a) In Vietnam, 73% of men smoke. Vietnam is a very poor country.
Why do you think so many men smoke?

b) In Vietnam, 4% of women smoke.
Why do you think there is such a large difference?
Are Vietnamese women more sensible?

c) Sweden has by far the lowest smoking rate for men.
It is a very wealthy country.
Can you think why it has a low rate?

23 In the world's poorest countries the percentage of smokers is rising rapidly.
In the world's richest countries it is falling.
Why do you think this is?

24 Here is a graph of the percentage of men who are smokers in India, compared with the time they spend at school in years.

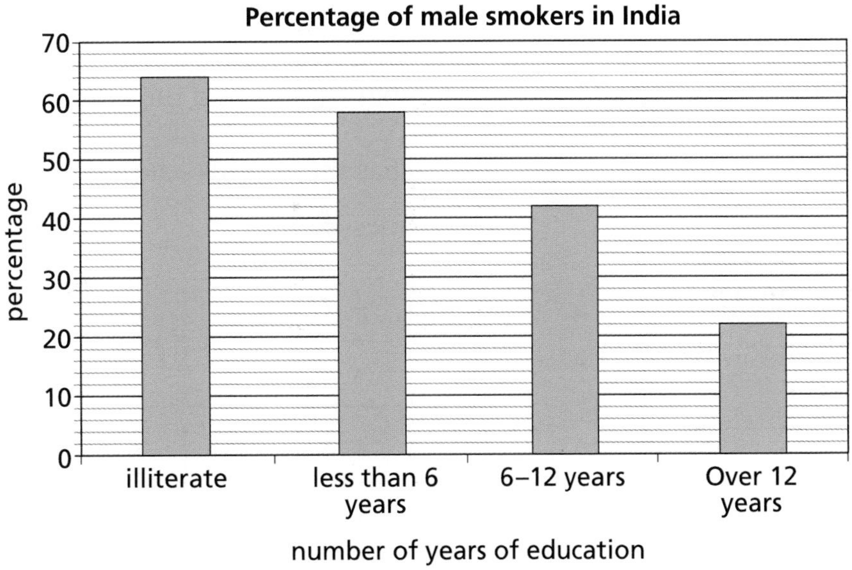

a) What do you think 'illiterate' means?

b) Write down the percentages in each category.

c) What do you notice?

d) Why do you think this is?

25 Now try Worksheet 6 *Jobs for smokers*.

26

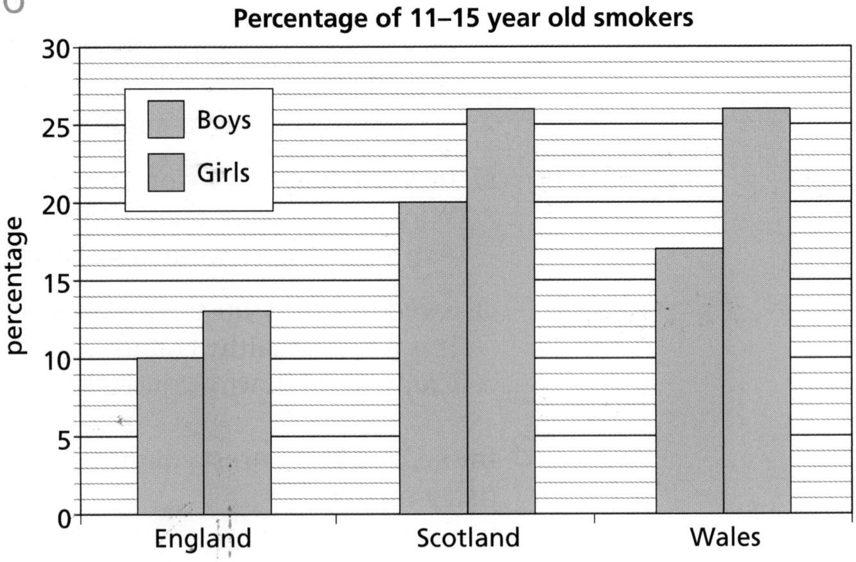

a) What percentage of boys smoke in England?

b) What percentage of boys smoke in Scotland?

c) What is the percentage difference between the two?

d) What do you notice about the difference between the number of boys and the number of girls smoking?

27 Nadim has these cards – hearts ♥, clubs ♣, diamonds ♦ and spades ♠:

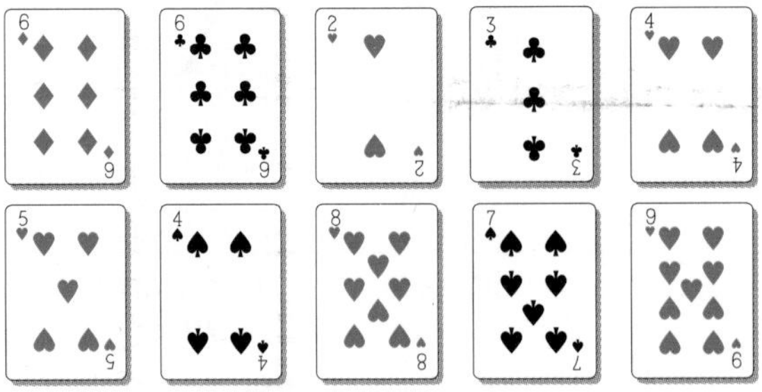

If he turned them all face down and took one card:

a) which is the suit he is **most** likely to pick?

b) which is the suit he is **least** likely to pick?

c) is the card more likely to be a black or a red suit?

There is no test for this unit.